CALGARY
SCIENCE
FUN GUIDE

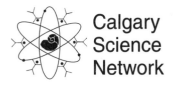

Calgary
Science
Network

BARE BONES PUBLISHING

The Publisher
Bare Bones Publishing
Suite 355, 305-4625 Varsity Drive NW
Calgary, Alberta T3A 0Z9

Acknowledgements
Cover design by Joyce Harris
Activity illustrations by Joyce Harris
Text design and editing by Linda Reynolds
Inputting and layout by Sika Patton and Peggy Penney
Printed and bound in Canada by Webcom Limited.

Primary financial support provided by Shell Canada Limited

 **Shell**

Donations also received from the Association of Professional Engineers Geologists and Geophysicists of Alberta (APEGGA) and Webcom Limited

Printed on recycled paper.

Canadian Cataloguing in Publication Data
Main entry under title:
        Calgary science fun guide
2nd ed.
Includes index.
ISBN 1-896865-02-X

        1. Science—Alberta—Calgary—Societies, etc.—Directories. 2. Science clubs—Alberta—Calgary—Directories. 3. Science museums—Alberta—Calgary—Directories. 4. Scientific recreations. I. Calgary Science Network

Q21.C34 1997   502'5'712338   C97-900957-X

CONTENTS

Shell Canada is proud to be a
major sponsor of the Calgary
Science Fun Guide.

At Shell, we believe doing
is the best part of learning.

We hope you enjoy the activities
in this educational guide!

INTRODUCTION

Science is exciting, stimulating and—above all—fun. Did you know it's all around us, in everyday things, from boiling an egg for breakfast to brushing your teeth at night? We at the Calgary Science Network (CSN) would like to introduce you to the wonders of science.

The CSN is a group of volunteers keen to stimulate curiosity about science in adults and kids—the scientists and technologists of tomorrow. In our increasingly technological world, it's becoming essential to nurture the inventive minds that will bring us new scientific and technological discoveries in the 21st century.

Have you or your kids ever wondered what makes helicopters fly, why goldfish have so many fins, or why apples go brown after they're peeled? If you try some of the great hands-on activities in this guide, you'll find out. We're including over 60 hands-on activities designed to teach through "doing", as kids learn best through tangible experiences. As their curiosity is aroused, we hope they'll delve deeper into the wonderful world of science and technology.

HOW TO USE THIS GUIDE

We've organized the guide as follows:
- lefthand pages — Calgary science and nature resources
- righthand pages — hands-on activities

Each hands-on activity is linked by topic to the Calgary resource opposite it. Most activities were written by CSN members or originally published in the *Greater Vancouver Science Fun Guide*. (Sincere thanks to SCIENCE WORLD British Columbia for permission to use these activities.) In the index on page 153, the activities are linked to the Alberta Education elementary and junior high school science curriculum units. We hope teachers find this useful.

ACKNOWLEDGEMENTS

We are very grateful to our primary sponsor, Shell Canada Limited, for the funds that enabled us to start this second edition of the *Calgary Science Fun Guide*. Thanks also to supporting sponsors, APEGGA and Webcom Limited. To the production team (Linda Reynolds, Joyce Harris, Sika Patton, Peggy Penney); CSN's volunteer Science Fun Guide committee (Beverley Cridland, Roland Dechesne, Linda Reynolds, Ken Ronak, Cathy Szata, Janis Webb and Leanne Wirch); and CSN members who wrote activities, our heartfelt thanks for the hard work and long hours needed to produce this terrific guide.

Martin Kirk, President, Calgary Science Network

AEROSPACE MUSEUM ASSOCIATION

WHO WE ARE

We are a non-profit society that is dedicated to preserving the aviation history of Alberta and Albertans, in particular Calgarians.

Aerospace Museum Association
4629 McCall Way N.E.
Calgary, Alberta T2E 8A5

Tel: (403) 250-3752
Fax: (403) 250-8399
World Wide Web: http://www.lexicom.ab.ca

Days and Hours

Open all year, except Christmas Day and New Year's Day. Monday to Sunday, 10:00 a.m. to 5:00 p.m.

Admission Fees

Family - $15.00; Adult - $6.00; Seniors and students (12-17) - $3.50
Children (6-11) - $2.00; Children under 6 - Free
Aviation Day (end of May/beginning of June) reduced admission; children free.

WHAT WE DO

We provide guided tours of our facility, which houses a unique aircraft collection. We have an ongoing aircraft collection policy, which enables us to add to our collection. Thirty types of engines are on display, from the rotary World War One engine to today's modern jet engine. Our twin-engine simulator gives visitors an opportunity to imagine being a pilot. The science of flight is part of our program and illustrated by such displays as the Avro Anson airplane wing display, which shows the internal structure of an airplane wing.

Programs Offered

School tours (from ECS to Grade 6) may be booked with two weeks notice.

Facilities

Museum, bookstore, giftshop. Aviation-related clubs may rent the facilities for meetings.

HELI-PAPER

WHAT YOU NEED
- A piece of paper 25 cm x 5 cm
- A paper clip

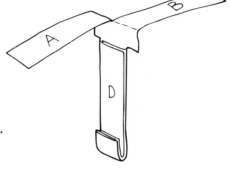

WHAT TO DO
1. Follow the pattern below. Cut along the solid lines and then fold on the dotted lines.
2. Fold A forward, B backward.
3. Fold C in and overlap it with D.
4. Then fold upward at E.
5. Go to a high place.
6. Lift your Heli-paper above your head with D towards the ground, as shown in the diagram, then drop it.

WHAT'S GOING ON?
You have made the type of "wing" used by helicopters. It is called a horizontal rotor. The shape of your rotor causes it to twist due to uneven drag on the paper surface. The rotor begins spinning and this reduces the pressure above the "wing". The pressure underneath the spinning rotor is greater and pushes up, allowing the helicopter to drift slowly down rather than falling quickly. Real helicopters *lift up* when the motor spins the rotor at tremendous speeds.

WHAT ELSE YOU CAN DO
Put a paper clip over the folded part at E. See if it changes the flight pattern.

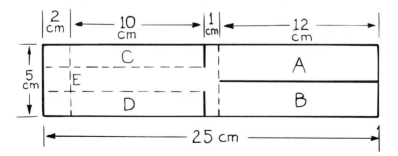

ALBERTA AGRICULTURE, FOOD AND RURAL DEVELOPMENT CONSERVATION AND DEVELOPMENT BRANCH

WHO WE ARE
We are a branch of the provincial government that ensures responsible stewardship of Alberta's soil and water resources.

Alberta Agriculture, Food and Rural Development
Conservation and Development Branch
Bag Service No. 1
Airdrie, Alberta   T4B 2C1

Tel: (403) 948-8512
Fax: (403) 948-2069
E-mail: mckinnom@agric.gov.ab.ca
World Wide Web: http://www.agric.gov.ab.ca

Resources
Resource materials available: *Conserving Soil for the Next Generation* (includes a teacher's guide). This topic is appropriate to many areas of the elementary school curriculum for Grades 4 to 6. Two *Living Soil* modules are also available: *The Living Soil - Renewable Resource,* a science module, *The Living Soil - Land Use and Society,* a social studies module.

Numerous videos and information sheets are available on loan from Alberta Agriculture district offices. Our website also offers a lot of interesting information.

OUR EARTH'S LIVING "SKIN"

WHAT YOU NEED
- 2 oranges

WHAT TO DO

1. To represent the amount of usable soil on Earth, begin with an orange. The orange represents the Earth, and the orange peel represents the surface of the Earth. Most of us think of this as mostly dirt or soil, but that is not the case!

2. Put one of the oranges aside.

3. Remove three-quarters of the peel from the other orange. This represents the amount of water on Earth.

4. From the remaining peel, remove half of it. This represents areas where there is little or no usable soil (bogs, deserts, cities, mountains).

5. Carefully peel away three-quarters of the remaining orange peel. This represents areas that are too hot, too cold, or too wet for farming.

6. Look at how much peel is left on your orange. This is how much usable soil we have on Earth. It is only one thirty-second of the Earth's surface!

7. Compare the unpeeled orange with this one.

WHAT'S GOING ON?

People take soil for granted because it seems to be everywhere we go. However, as this experiment has shown, that is definitely **not** the case. We need the soil to survive because it supports the plant and animal life we eat. Soil takes hundreds of thousands of years to form, yet it can be lost and returned to the oceans through erosion in a matter of hours. It is important to appreciate our soil, and to take its conservation very seriously!

WHAT ELSE TO DO

Peel the remaining orange and share the fruit. While you are enjoying it, think about the wonderful soil that the orange trees grew in.

BE CAREFUL!

Make sure you wash the oranges before eating them.

ALBERTA LUNG ASSOCIATION

WHO WE ARE

The Alberta Lung Association is a non-profit health agency involved in promoting lung health and preventing lung disease.

Alberta Lung Association
302, 609 - 14th Street N.W.
Calgary, Alberta   T2N 2A1

Health Initiatives Department
Tel: (403) 283-1333
Health information line: 1-800-661-LUNG
Fax: (403) 283-1558

WHAT WE DO

We provide programs and information on lung-related diseases and how to prevent them.

Programs Offered

Blast (Building Leadership for Action in Schools Today) Conference is a high-energy, three-day program where delegates learn leadership skills and develop action plans. The delegates return to their schools and help empower Alberta youth (Grades 7 to 9) to make informed decisions about issues related to their health: clean air, the environment, tobacco and advocacy, peer support and lung health.

The Smoke-Free Class is an education and awareness program focussing on students who will graduate in the year 2000 and after 2000. Teaching packages are available free of charge and are designed to teach students about the hazards of tobacco and the benefits of choosing a healthy lifestyle by remaining smoke free.

We also run an Asthma Camp for kids, Stop Smoking classes for parents, and distribute health education materials on tobacco, lung health and air quality.

Resources

Books, newsletter, teacher kits, speakers, information sheets, portable exhibits, 1-800-661-LUNG health information line. Our Teacher's Resource List contains information about videos, pamphlets, posters and additional material to supplement the Smoke-Free Class program.

A HUFF AND A PUFF

WHAT YOU NEED
- A large plastic bag
- A marker pen to write on the bag
- A plastic funnel
- A 2-litre measuring jug full of water

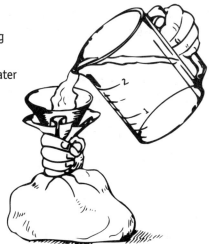

WHAT TO DO
1. Grasp the top of the bag as if you were going to blow it up and burst it.

2. Make the mouth opening wide enough to breathe into with your mouth open.

3. Squeeze all the air out of the bag.

4. Breathe twice normally.

5. On the third breath, breathe in as much air as you can.

6. Put the plastic bag to your open mouth.

7. Pinch your nose and breathe out hard all at once into the bag. (Remember to keep your mouth open.)

8. Bend forward and squeeze every last drop of air out of your lungs.

9. Close the bag tightly at the top.

10. Slide your hand down the neck of the bag, pushing the air to the foot, until the bag has completely expanded.

11. Draw a line on the bag where you're holding it, in case you lose your grip.

12. Hold the bag firmly and put the funnel in the neck of the bag. (You can let the air escape.)

13. Carefully pour water from the measuring jug into the bag, until it's as full of water as it was of air.

14. Make a note of how much water you poured into the bag. This will tell you how much air your lungs can hold—your lung capacity.

WHAT ELSE YOU CAN DO
Have your friends try this, then compare your lung capacity with theirs.

ALBERTA PALAEONTOLOGICAL SOCIETY

WHO WE ARE

We are a society whose members have a keen interest in fossils, and who keep themselves informed of new discoveries and various other aspects of palaeontology.

Alberta Palaeontological Society
P.O. Box 35111, Sarcee Postal Outlet
Calgary, Alberta   T3E 7C7

Tel: (403) 547-0182

Meeting Place and Time

Meetings held the third Friday of the month except June, July and August. Room B108, Mount Royal College, Calgary, 7:30 p.m.

Membership Fees

Single $15.00/year, Family $20.00/year.

WHAT WE DO

We hold three field trips a year, in June, July and August. Our *Bulletin* is published quarterly and includes articles from members, book reviews, etc. Meetings include a short business section, but most of the time is devoted to a guest speaker and their presentation. Various topics on palaeontology are covered throughout the year.

Programs Offered

Adult, family.

Resources

Newsletter, speakers, portable exhibits.

Facilities

Classroom/science room. We have a library from which members can borrow publications on short loan. We also have a fossil collection available as an educational guide for members.

LEAVING A TRACE

WHAT YOU NEED
- 500 mL fresh play dough (homemade or purchased)
- Empty margarine tub
- 60 mL vegetable oil
- 250 mL plaster of Paris (powder)
- 125 mL water
- Item to make a fossil cast of (chicken bone, leaf, stick, seed, plastic toy, etc.)

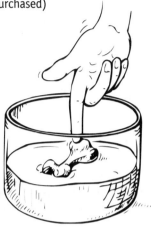

WHAT TO DO
1. Pack the play dough into the empty margarine tub until it is about one half full. Make the surface smooth.

2. Coat the item you are going to make a cast of with a thin film of oil. Make sure it is thoroughly coated so the play dough will not stick to it.

3. Press the object firmly into the play dough, making a clear, deep imprint.

4. Remove the object and set the play dough aside for two days so you have a hard "fossil" mould.

5. When completely hardened, coat the "fossil" mould with more oil, again making sure it is thoroughly covered.

6. Mix the plaster of Paris and the water together (be sure to follow the safety precautions on the plaster of Paris box).

7. Pour the mixture over the top of the mould and set aside to dry in a warm spot. This will take a few days but do not be impatient because the plaster must be completely set before being moved.

8. When set, carefully separate the plaster and the play dough. Now you have a cast, which has the outward shape of the item used to make the mould.

WHAT'S GOING ON?
The play dough represents the soft mud that was once the ground millions of years ago. Plants and animals made imprints in this mud and if nothing filled them in before they hardened, the imprints eventually became fossil moulds similar to the one you made. The plaster of Paris that you used represents the sediments that later filled in the moulds and made cast fossils. Common cast fossils are leaf imprints, footprints and shells. Palaeontologists can trace the history of our planet's life millions of years ago by studying these fossils.

ALBERTA WOMEN'S SCIENCE NETWORK

WHO WE ARE

We are an umbrella organization for Alberta organizations promoting women in science and technology.

Alberta Women's Science Network
P.O. Box 6912, Station D
Calgary, Alberta   T2P 2G1

Tel: (403) 282-6431
Fax: (403) 284-4750
Toll free: 1-888-880-1788
E-mail: awsn@awsn.com
World Wide Web: http://www.awsn.com

WHAT WE DO

We mentor young women considering careers in science and technology, and strive to improve networking among women in science in Alberta by representing the following groups:

- AWES — Association of Women in Engineering and Science—Edmonton and Calgary
- WISEST — Women in Scholarship, Engineering, Science and Technology, University of Alberta
- UC-WISE — Women in Science and Engineering, University of Calgary
- UAWS — University of Alberta Women in Science and Engineering
- Scientific Literacy Committee — Mount Royal College
- Operation Minerva — an organization of women mentors offering job-shadowing programs for junior high girls in communities throughout Alberta

Programs Offered

Elementary, junior and senior high school, community, adult, family.

Resources

A Lending library that has print materials, teaching aids, videos, workbooks, files, information sheets, reports, abstracts and proceedings relevant to women and careers in science. Individuals, schools and organizations may borrow materials for use at conferences or for research and education. We publish a quarterly newsletter and have a catalogue of resources available.

POP CAN PORSCHE

WHAT YOU NEED
- Pop can
- Hammer
- Nail
- Rubber bands
- Pencil
- Plastic bead
- Wire (bent coat hanger)
- Popsicle stick
- Plastic disc (cut from an ice cream container)

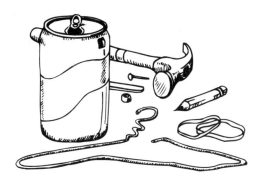

WHAT TO DO
1. Using a hammer and nail, make a hole in the bottom of a pop can. The hole must be big enough for a rubber band to pass through.

2. Cut a plastic disc (from an ice cream bucket or lid) to fit the top of a pop can. Poke a hole through the centre of this disk.

3. Thread a rubber band through a plastic bead, then through the centre of the plastic disk. Then loop it over a pencil to secure it.

4. Using a long wire hook, pull the rubber band through the top of the pop can and out the bottom. Loop this end of the rubber band over a Popsicle stick so it cannot be pulled back into the can. (Break the stick so its length is less than the can's diameter.)

5. Wind the pencil up until the rubber band is tight. Set the Porsche on the floor, so that as the pencil tries to unwind, it pushes on the floor.

6. Release and watch your Pop Can Porsche roll away. If it slips and spins on the floor, wrap rubber bands outside the can to act as tires.

WHAT'S GOING ON?
As the rubber band unwinds, it tries to turn the Popsicle stick and the pencil. The friction between the Popsicle stick and the can is too great to move the stick. The pencil can move because the bead and plastic disc have less friction between them. However, when the pencil tries to turn, it pushes on the floor (which pushes back) and so the only way the rubber band can unwind is to roll the can forward. As the can rolls, the potential energy that is stored in the wound rubber band is transformed into motion (kinetic energy) and heat. The can will roll if the energy stored in the wound rubber band produces a force great enough to overcome the force of friction between the bead and the disk and between the can and the floor.

ANN AND SANDY CROSS CONSERVATION AREA

WHO WE ARE
We are an area of land (4800 acres) in the foothills southwest of Calgary, which was donated to educate visitors about preservation and conservation. The area has beautiful scenery, elk, moose, deer, coyotes, bears, cougars, red-tail hawks — all waiting to be discovered!

Ann and Sandy Cross Conservation Area
Box 20, Site 23, RR 8
Calgary, Alberta   T2J 2T9

Tel: (403) 931-2042
Fax: (403) 931-2726

Days and Hours
Area open during daylight hours; building open only when booked.

Size of Groups Accommodated
Maximum 60.

WHAT WE DO
We focus on providing groups with an increased awareness of conservation and preservation of wildlife and natural habitats.

Programs Offered
Preschool, elementary, junior and senior high school, post-secondary credit, teacher training, adult, family, community, senior citizen, youth groups.
Tours: Tours can be arranged for groups, but you can walk on your own, as long as you have booked ahead. Individuals can hike in the area, but **must** call (403) 931-2042 first. **Types of Field Trips:** Volunteer-led walks focusing on area ecology for Grades 1 to 9. Walks are 3.5 to 4 km long and incorporate wildlife observation. Pre- and post-visit activities available. **Summer Camps:** Nature Nuts — week long day camps for ages 7 to 12. Call for details.

Facilities
Exhibits and displays, live animals (outside!), trails.

LITTER CRITTERS

WHAT YOU NEED

- 1 funnel
- 1 glass jar
- Black construction paper
- Desk lamp
- Pile of freshly gathered leaf litter
- Masking tape

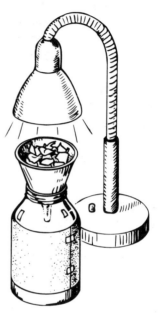

WHAT TO DO

1. Wrap glass jar in black paper and secure with tape.
2. Place funnel in jar opening.
3. Place leaf litter in funnel.
4. Shine lamp over leaf litter.

WHAT'S GOING ON?

Tiny critters live in the litter layer on the forest floor. After an hour or so, check to see if any litter layer creatures have fallen into the jar. Why would the animals move out of their litter layer (too hot or too light)? Describe the animals you see and maybe group them according to the number of legs they have or how they move.

Remember—when you have finished looking at the animals, put them back into the wild!

ASSOCIATION OF PROFESSIONAL ENGINEERS, GEOLOGISTS AND GEOPHYSICISTS OF ALBERTA (APEGGA)

WHO WE ARE
We serve society by regulating, enhancing and providing leadership in the practice of the member professions in Alberta. We represent more than 29,000 engineers, geologists and geophysicists in Alberta who use their expertise in such areas as diverse as environmental technology, resource development, construction, public works, transportation, agriculture, manufacturing and processing.

APEGGA, Calgary Office
1600 Life Plaza
734 - 7 Avenue S.W.
Calgary, Alberta   T2P 3P8

Student Outreach Program
Tel: (403) 262-7714
Fax: (403) 269-2787

WHAT WE DO
We are acknowledged by educators and students as one of the most proactive professional organizations in the province. Our career counselling volunteers keep young people informed of opportunities in science and technology, with an emphasis on how APEGGA professions impact their lives. More than 200 volunteers are involved in classroom visits, judging science fairs, mentoring and other activities. APEGGA provides awards and scholarships for students (high school through graduate study level), honours excellence in science and math education with the Teacher Awards Program, and is working to ensure Alberta's science and math curricula meet the highest standards.

We have also taken a leading role in promoting the value of science and math to Albertans during National Science and Technology Week by sponsoring public events and working cooperatively with organizations such as the Science Alberta Foundation, the Calgary Science Network and the Edmonton Space & Science Centre.

Programs Offered
Elementary, junior and senior high school.

SLITHERY SLIME

WHAT YOU NEED

- White glue (Elmer's school glue is best)
- Borax
- Water
- 2 medium-sized plastic containers
- Food colouring

WHAT TO DO

1. Mix 125 mL water with 125 mL glue in one container.
2. Add the food colouring.
3. In another container, mix 250 mL water with 45 mL borax.
4. Add 60 mL of the borax solution to the glue solution and mix it with your fingers.
5. Mush the mixture around with your hands until it thickens. Then put it on a table and knead it with your hands until there is no obvious liquid on the surface of the slime.
6. Stretch and squish the slime to observe how it behaves. Is it a solid or a liquid? Does it feel warm or cold? It should feel cold, especially when it's stretched very thinly. How thin can you stretch the slime before it breaks? Does it stretch better when you pull on it quickly or when you pull on it slowly?
7. Store slime in a resealable bag and keep it in a cool place.

WHAT'S GOING ON?

Chemical reactions can be classified by whether they produce or absorb heat. The reaction that makes the slime is caused from heat being absorbed from our hands as we handle it This is why it feels cold and slimy. The more the slime is handled, the harder it gets.

The slime is a special kind of substance called a polymer. Polymers are also known as plastics.

ASSOCIATION OF WOMEN IN ENGINEERING AND SCIENCE (AWES)

WHO WE ARE
We are a networking support group of professional female engineers and scientists who meet regularly.

Association of Women in Engineering and Science
Box 6912, Station D
Calgary, Alberta   T2P 2G1

Tel: (403) 259-7937
World Wide Web: http://www.awsn.com

Meeting Place and Time
First Wednesday of the month, 5:00 p.m., Greenstreet Restaurant, 815 - 7 Avenue S.W., Calgary. Other events as announced.

Membership Fees
$30.00/year.

WHAT WE DO
We hold seminars and luncheons for members in addition to our monthly networking sessions at Greenstreet Restaurant. We send out a newsletter to members seven times a year. We also have volunteers who talk to students of all ages about careers in science and engineering, judge at science fairs and act as mentors.

Programs Offered
Preschool, elementary, junior and senior high school, adult.

Resources
Newsletter, books, speakers, presentations, portable exhibits.

CRASH TEST CARS

WHAT YOU NEED

- Scissors
- 2 bulldog clips (2-3 cm)
- Plasticine or Blue-Tak
- 1 thin plastic straw
- 2 books
- Several patterns for circles (different sizes)
- Large, flat surface (table top works well)
- Sheet of stiff poster board (large enough to trace several circles for wheels)
- Ruler or long, thin stiff piece of cardboard (cut from a cereal box)

WHAT TO DO

1. To make the body of your car: take the ruler or cardboard and clip the bulldog clips near each end. Cut two 3-cm pieces of straw for the axles. Insert the axles through the holes in the front and back bulldog clips.

2. To make the wheels: take the poster board and cut out four big wheels (about 6-cm radius) and four small ones (about 4-cm radius). Mark the approximate centre of each.

3. Decide what wheels you want to use first. You could start with four of the same size (large or small). To put wheels onto axles, take a small amount of Plasticine and place near the centre of the wheel. Stick this onto the end of the straw. Do this for all four wheels.

4. To make the test ramp: have an adult help you put the two books under the legs of the table at one end. Let your car go from the high end of the ramp. What path does it take?

5. Now change the wheels and experiment with different sizes (e.g., big on the back and small on the front, big on one side and small on the other). How does the path and speed differ with each change?

WHAT'S GOING ON?

You have just completed testing your car in much the same way an engineeer would. To get a vehicle or any other machine to perform a certain way, engineers design tests to find what works best for a particular job. From the results of their tests, they know what must be changed and what can be kept the same in their design. From your observations, what combination of wheels would work best for a car that you wanted to go fast?

BAT CONSERVATION SOCIETY OF CANADA

WHO WE ARE
We are a federally and provincially registered non-profit volunteer organization dedicated to the preservation and conservation of bats and their habitat in Canada.

Bat Conservation Society of Canada
P.O. Box 56042
Airways Postal Outlet
Calgary, Alberta   T2E 8K5

Tel: (403) 860-BATS
E-mail: BCSC@cadvision.com

Membership Fees

Youth (Little Brown Bats)	$ 10.00
Senior (Silver-haired Bats)	$ 10.00
Basic (Big Brown Bats)	$ 25.00
Annual Renewal (Hoary Bat!)	$ 20.00
Friends of BCSC (Red Bats)	$ 50.00
Corporate (Spotted Bats)	$100.00

WHAT WE DO
We provide information about the preservation and conservation of bats through lectures, using various types of visual aides and interesting, technological devices. We also provide information on nuisance problems.

Programs Offered
Preschool, elementary, junior high, senior high, youth, adult, family, community, handicapped and senior citizen groups throughout Alberta and British Columbia. Several free public programs are offered annually in various locations. Call for information on programs, memberships and general information on bats.

Resources
Newsletter (included in membership), speakers, presentations.

BAT HAVEN

WHAT YOU NEED

- Staples or glue
- Black paint or stain
- Wood, any kind, new or used:
  - 1 piece of lumber or plywood for the front and back
  - 1 piece of 2.5 cm x 5 cm lumber for the ceiling and walls
  - 1 piece of 2.5 cm x 10 cm lumber for the roof
- 1 piece of fibreglass window screening, same dimensions as the back wall of the bat house
- A helpful adult

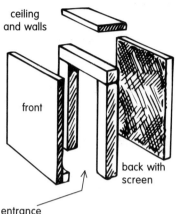

ceiling and walls

front

back with screen

entrance

WHAT TO DO

1. With the help of an adult, cut the first piece of wood into pieces about 35 cm x 55 cm for the front and back. The front should be about 2 cm shorter than the back.

2. Attach a strip of wood to the bottom inside of the front. This makes the entrance to the bat house smaller so that no other animals can get in. This entrance should be 2 cm (from the front inside to the back).

3. Staple the fibreglass screen to the inside of the back of the house. This makes a good place for the bats to hold onto.

4. Cut the 2.5 cm x 5 cm piece of wood into three pieces—one for the ceiling and two for the side walls.

5. Glue or nail the house together, then stain or paint it.

6. The house is small inside—5 cm front to back—and the bottom is open.

WHERE TO PUT IT

Mount it facing south on a tall pole or tree, or the south side of a building—the sunnier the better. Put it near open water if you can, where there are lots of insects (bat food). Make sure there are no obstructions underneath.

BE PATIENT

It will take some time before bats actually use the house.

BUTTERFIELD ACRES CHILDREN'S FARM

WHO WE ARE

We are a working farm that is open to the public for pre-booked visits, which consist of many different activity stations—all the things you'd do if you actually lived on a farm!

Butterfield Acres Children's Farm
Box 21, Site 7, S.S. 1
Calgary, Alberta   T2M 4N3
[3 km north of Crowchild Trail on Rocky Ridge Road (101 Street N.W.)]

Tel: (403) 239-0638
Fax: (403) 239-0638
Info Line: (403) 547-3595

Admission Fees and Hours

We are open all year. Please call for specific information about each program as times and fees vary.

WHAT WE DO

We have a variety of programs available, all very child-oriented and geared towards a "real" farm experience for families, school children and preschoolers.

Programs Offered

General public, groups, church, office and family events. **Types of Field Trips:** *Real Life Farm Experience! Happy Homesteading, Country Christmas, Winter Fun* (includes hay rides, tobogganing and skating, fire pit/roast), *Fall Pumpkin Hunts*. **Types of Outreach Programs:** Farm Corral petting zoo for special events; Pony Rides for special events. **Summer Camps:** Be a real farm kid for a week! Camps for 3- to 11-year-old children have fun, educational, age-appropriate farm activities.

Resources

Teacher information package.

Facilities

Exhibits and displays (hands-on), interpretive nature hikes, live animals, outdoor fire pits, snack bar, picnic shelter with indoor fire pit, picnic and playgrounds, toboggan hills, skating pond, Birthday Barn.

HUMBUG!

WHAT YOU NEED
- Paper or foam cup
- Piece of thin card
- Waxed paper
- Elastic band
- Insects

WHAT TO DO
1. Use the cup and piece of thin card to capture the insect you want to study.

2. Slide a piece of waxed paper between the cup and the cardboard, remove the cardboard and secure the waxed paper using an elastic band.

3. Hold the cup next to your ear. Can you hear the insect's wings beating? Do different insects sound alike or different?

4. Carefully release each insect once you have listened to it.

WHAT'S GOING ON?
The cup acts as an amplifier, increasing the volume of the sound of an insect's wings beating. The beating wings cause the air in the amplifier chamber to vibrate; in turn, the air moves the waxed paper covering the cup.

An insect that works especially well in the chamber, and that is easy to catch, is the mosquito. A mosquito's wings flap 300 times per second. A honeybee's wings flap about 250 times per second. A fly's wings flap 190 times per second. Do you think these insects would sound different in the chamber? Why? Does it have something to do with how fast their wings flap?

WHAT ELSE YOU CAN DO
Try imitating the sounds you hear.

CALGARY AQUARIUM SOCIETY

WHO WE ARE
We are a group of hobbyists offering information and encouragement to people interested in acquiring and maintaining tropical and salt-water aquaria.

Calgary Aquarium Society
Box 63180, 2604 Kensington Road N.W.
Calgary, Alberta   T2N 4S5

Tel: (403) 249-8733
Membership:
Tel: (403) 256-2445

Membership Fees
Annual: $24.00 (regular), $14.00 (junior—18 and under).

Meeting Place and Time
Crescent Heights Community Centre, 1101 - 2 St N.W., Calgary; second Tuesday of each month at 7:30 p.m. Everyone welcome. No meetings in July and August.

WHAT WE DO
Our monthly meetings include special workshops or presentations; activities include jar shows, fish auctions, special home shows and awards, and the Annual Labour Day Weekend "fish show" and auction, as well as speakers on a variety of subjects.

Programs Offered
Adult, new aquarist, junior aquarist. The possibility of establishing special subgroups, such as a youth group, exists, if there is sufficient interest. We also offer fish breeding and aquatic horticulture programs.

Resources
Calgary Aquarium Society Magazine, extensive library for members.

GET FRESH (WATER)

Note: Adult supervision is required for this activity.

WHAT YOU NEED
- 250 mL water
- 5 mL salt
- A glass or enamel pan with lid
- 2 clean glasses

WHAT TO DO
1. Put 250 mL of tap water into the pan.
2. Add 5 mL of salt and stir until dissolved.
3. Pour a small amount (about 10 ml) of salt water into one of the cups.
4. Put the lid on the pan and bring the water to a boil on the stove.
5. When the water is boiling, carefully remove the lid and turn it over.
6. Pour the water drops on the underside of the lid into the empty glass.
7. Replace the lid to collect more water drops.
8. Repeat Steps 5 to 7 until you have about 10 mL of water in the glass.
9. Remove the pan from the stove.
10. Set the cup of water aside to cool.
11. Taste the water in the two cups. How does it differ?

WHAT'S GOING ON?
Water is a precious resource, but most of Earth's water is salty and can't be used for drinking. However, salt can be removed from water, as you saw in this activity. Water vapour evaporated then condensed on the underside of the lid, but salt can't do this, so it stayed in the pan. This makes the water you collected drinkable. Scientists are currently experimenting with a similar procedure on a large scale in what are known as desalinization plants. So far, it is too expensive to be a practical way of getting fresh drinking water.

WHAT ELSE YOU CAN DO
Some fish can live quite happily in salt water, but others can only survive in freshwater. Next time you're at the pet store, ask if they have salt-water fish for you to observe. Do you think the salt-water fish would survive if you put them in an aquarium filled with tap water? Why not?

CALGARY CONSORTIUM FOR ELEMENTARY SCIENCE EDUCATION
(A SERVICE OF THE CALGARY SCIENCE NETWORK)

WHO WE ARE

We are a partnership of the Calgary Science Network, the Calgary Board of Education and the Calgary Catholic School Board, with major funding from the Calgary Foundation.

Calgary Consortium for Elementary Science Education
c/o Geological Survey of Canada
3303 - 33 Street N.W.
Calgary, Alberta   T2L 2A7

Tel: (403) 230-1431
Fax: (403) 230-8488
World Wide Web: www.cadvision.com/calg_sci_net

WHAT WE DO

For the past three years, we have organized workshops on the new science curriculum for elementary science teachers.

Programs Offered

The Making Connections Summer Institute is held during the first week of July. Making Connections Short Courses are held after school or Saturday mornings. Science Symposium is held two evenings in October. These workshops are facilitated by volunteer scientists, sometimes in conjunction with teachers. The goal of the workshops is to further teachers' understanding of science theory while providing accessible, innovative activities to enhance classroom learning.

SPELLBINDING SPAGHETTI

WHAT YOU NEED

- Water
- Large clear glass jar or vase
- Food colouring
- Baking soda
- Large spoon
- 3 strands of dried, uncooked spaghetti
- Vinegar

WHAT TO DO

1. Put 750 mL of water in the glass jar or vase. Add a few drops of food colouring, if you wish.
2. Add 30 mL of baking soda. Stir well.
3. Break three strands of spaghetti into small pieces of various lengths and add them to the jar.
4. Stir in 80 mL of vinegar and watch what happens. Does the spaghetti float and sink? When the spaghetti starts to slow down, add more vinegar.

WHAT'S GOING ON?

A chemical reaction between the baking soda and the vinegar produces carbon dioxide gas that forms bubbles on the spaghetti. The bubbles float the spaghetti to the top. At the top, the bubbles burst, the spaghetti sinks, and the process starts all over again.

WHAT ELSE YOU CAN DO

Cook some pasta to observe if it expands when it is cooked. Pasta is a high-carbohydrate (starch) food. As it cooks, the molecules that make up the starch relax and unfold, forming new bonds and creating a network that traps water molecules. The result? The pasta doubles in size.

CALGARY HORTICULTURAL SOCIETY

WHO WE ARE

We are a society devoted to the beginner to intermediate enthusiastic gardener. We provide an opportunity to exchange ideas and develop skills.

Calgary Horticultural Society
208 - 50th Avenue S.W.
Calgary, Alberta   T2S 2S1

Tel: (403) 287-3469
Fax: (403) 287-6986
World Wide Web: http://www.calhort.org

Meeting Place and Time

The Orpheus Theatre in the Campus Building at SAIT. Every third Tuesday, from September through June (except December), 7:30 p.m. Members free. Non-members always welcome with a suggested donation of $3.00.

Membership Fees

$20.00 single; $25.00 family; seniors discount available.

WHAT WE DO

The Calgary Horticultural Society (CHS) was founded in 1907 to encourage gardening in Calgary. Today with over 3000 members, the CHS is devoted to sharing information with the enthusiastic beginner as well as the intermediate gardener. We provide monthly speakers, workshops, newsletters, open gardens, bus tours, library, members-only Spring and Fall plant exchanges and discounts at garden centres and related businesses. The Calgary Horticultural Society published the best selling book, *The Calgary Gardener—The Essential Guide to Gardening in Alberta's Chinook Country*.

Programs Offered

Adult, senior citizen.

Resources

Books, newsletter, memberships.

Facilities

Library, bookstore.

COMPOSTING APPLES AND ORANGES

WHAT YOU NEED

- 4 slices of apple or pieces of orange peel
- A clear plastic bag
- Transparent tape
- 2 pickle jars
- A large spoon
- Soil

WHAT TO DO

1. Place two identical slices of apple or orange peel in a clear plastic bag. Tape the bag shut to seal it.
2. Fill the jars with soil and label them 1 and 2. Use the spoon to dig a hole in jar 1, and bury the wrapped fruit.
3. Dig a hole in jar 2 and bury two similar unwrapped pieces of fruit or peel.
4. Moisten the soil in both jars with water.
5. Water the jars every other day for a week, and loosen the soil gently with the spoon. Try not to disturb the unwrapped fruit or bag of wrapped fruit.
6. At the end of one week, look in the jar. Write down what you see.
7. Carefully scoop out the fruit, leaving the wrapped fruit in the plastic. What changes do you see? Write them down.
8. After you've noted the changes, bury the fruit again.
9. Leave the jars for another week, then write down what you see.

WHAT'S GOING ON?

"Compost" forms when organic matter decays or rots. The decay of organic matter happens naturally due to decomposers like bacteria, fungi, earthworms and snails. However, they require oxygen to live. The fruit in the plastic bag is how most of our garbage is disposed of—in plastic bags taken to a landfill. Plastic bags slow or stop the breakdown process because they prevent oxygen and some decomposers from reaching the organic matter.

Most gardeners like to use compost in their yards as it enriches the soil. They use grass clippings, leaves and other vegetable matter to make their compost. By doing this, they reduce the number of plastic bags going to the landfill.

WHAT ELSE YOU CAN DO

Try other kinds of fruits and vegetables in your composter and note how long each takes to decompose. Try to predict which of them will take the same time.

CALGARY HUMANE SOCIETY

WHO WE ARE

We are a non-profit, volunteer-based organization dedicated to improving the welfare of animals through programs and services in sheltering, education, protection and advocacy.

Calgary Humane Society
1323 - 36 Avenue N.E.
Calgary, Alberta   T2E 6T6

Tel: (403) 250-7722
Fax: (403) 291-9818

Meeting Place and Time

1323 - 36 Avenue N.E., variable times.

Membership Fees

Senior (over 65), $8.00; Family, $25.00; Corporate, $100.00; Individual, $20.00; Individual Lifetime, $150.00.

WHAT WE DO

Apart from Shelter programs, we provide educational opportunities, ranging from pet care to humane issues for many age groups.

Programs Offered

Elementary, junior and senior high school, teacher training, adult, community, youth groups. **Tours:** Age-appropriate programs including an Animal Shelter tour and then a talk with activities (up to 30 people). **Workshops:** Kids for Animals Club for kids aged 8 to 16 years.

Resources

Books, newsletter, teacher kits, memberships, information sheets.

Facilities

Classroom, live animals.

ANIMAL FRIGHT DISTANCE

WHAT YOU NEED

- Paper
- Pencil or pen
- Rocks or pieces of cloth to use as markers

WHAT TO DO

1. Go for a walk in your local park, in the woods or where you might expect to see some animals.

2. When you see an animal, such as a squirrel or a raccoon, note its exact location. (If you find a landmark such as a tree or a big rock it will help you remember the location.)

3. Walk slowly towards the animal while holding the marker in your hand.

4. When the animal moves away from you, drop the marker.

5. Pace out the distance between the marker and where the animal was just before it moved or ran away. This is the "fright distance".

6. Record the fright distance and the type of animal you saw.

7. Find the average fright distance for a particular type of animal.

8. Look for other animals and compare their fright distances.

WHAT'S GOING ON?

You can tell the difference between tame and wild animals by how easily they are frightened. For example, birds are very timid creatures. Sudden or quick movements cause them to take flight. A bird will allow you to get only so close and then it will fly away. Some birds tend to be more timid than others. Fright distance varies with the type of bird and whether or not a bird is used to having human beings around.

CALGARY PHILHARMONIC ORCHESTRA

WHO WE ARE
We are an organization catering to people of all ages who enjoy different kinds of music.

Calgary Philharmonic Orchestra
205 - 8th Avenue S.E.
Calgary, Alberta   T2G 0K9

Tel: (403) 571-0270
Fax: (403) 294-7424

WHAT WE DO
The CPO offers several programs catering to all ages in the Calgary community. Especially relevant for children and their families, are our Young Peoples' concerts, featuring prominent Canadian children's entertainers, and our education concerts. They are one-hour concerts adapted to the needs and curriculum of elementary school students. These programs are extremely popular, with bookings being made up to a year in advance.

Programs offered
Elementary, junior high school, adult, family, community.

Resources
Teacher kits.

Facilities
Concert hall.

MAKING WIND INSTRUMENTS

WHAT YOU NEED

- Old garden hose
- Funnel
- Scissors
- Many glass pop bottles
- Water

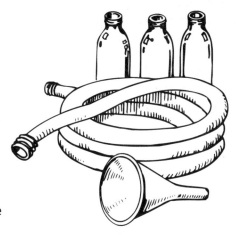

WHAT TO DO

French Horn

1. Place the funnel in the cut-off end of the hose.
2. Coil the hose in the shape of a French Horn.
3. Buzz your lips and blow into the tap attachment end of the hose.
4. Cut the hose to raise the pitch.

Caruba Tube

1. Hold the end of the hose and swing it quickly in the air to produce a pitch.
2. Cut the end of the hose to raise the pitch.

Wind Orchestra

1. Line up the bottles and fill them with water, from a few drops in the first one to a full bottle for the last one.
2. Blow across the top of the bottles, as you would with a flute, and create tunes with different pitches.

WHAT'S GOING ON?

In an orchestra, musicians make air vibrate to produce musical notes in three main ways—with strings, pipes or by hitting a surface. In a wind instrument, like the ones in this activity, the note depends on the length of the pipe and the materials it is made from.

WHAT ELSE YOU CAN DO

Try making some stringed instruments, using rubber bands on cake pans. What else can you use to make a stringed instrument? What could you use to make instruments like the drums or xylophone in an orchestra, where notes are produced by hitting a surface?

CALGARY POLICE SERVICE INTERPRETIVE CENTRE

WHO WE ARE
We are an educational, entertaining, hands-on facility that focuses on crime, the consequences of crime and the role of police in the community.

Calgary Police Service Interpretative Centre
    2nd Floor, 316 - 7th Avenue S.E.
Mailing address: 133 - 6th Avenue S.E.
    Calgary, Alberta   T2G 4Z1

Tel: (403) 268-4566
Fax: (403) 974-0508

Days and Hours
Summer: Monday to Thursday, 9:00 a.m. to 4:00 p.m., Saturday, noon to 4:00 p.m. Winter: Monday, Wednesday, 9:00 a.m. to 4:00 p.m., Saturday, 11:00 a.m. to 4:00 p.m., Sunday, noon to 4:00 p.m.

Admission Fees
Adults 18 and over - $2.00
Children under 18 and senior citizens - free.

WHAT WE DO
Provide tours and hands-on programs dealing with crime. Although the programs are geared to young people, they are of interest to all ages.

Programs Offered
Tours: Self-guided. Most exhibits are interactive. Challenging, educational interactive computer and video exhibits. Exhibits on forensics. **Special Programs:** Forensic science program, *Where's the Evidence,* dovetails well with Grade 6 science curriculum. Grade 5-9 teachers can book this program. Although not essential, teachers are strongly encouraged to visit the centre before the field trip, to prepare assignment sheets for their students.

Resources
Teacher kits, slide shows/videos/films.

Facilities
Combined museum and interpretive centre.

FINGERPRINT DETECTIVE

WHAT YOU NEED

- Glass
- Ink pad
- Paper
- Talcum powder
- Tissue
- Magnifying glass
- Paintbrush (fluffy, wide-tipped)

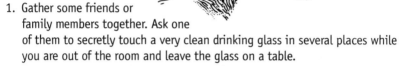

WHAT TO DO

1. Gather some friends or family members together. Ask one of them to secretly touch a very clean drinking glass in several places while you are out of the room and leave the glass on a table.

2. Return to the room to play detective and find out who touched the glass. Make a record of each "suspect's" fingertips by getting each person to roll their fingers on an ink pad. Then, one at a time, put the outside edges of their fingers on a piece of paper, and roll their fingers in towards their bodies to make a print of a large part of their fingers. They mustn't press too hard, and should roll their fingers gently in one direction.

3. Pick up the used drinking glass with a tissue. Be sure not to get your own fingerprints on the glass.

4. Place the glass on a sheet of paper. Dip the paintbrush into the talcum powder and gently dust one of the fingerprints on the glass. Brush in the direction of the ridges only enough to reveal the fingerprint pattern.

5. Use a magnifying glass to compare the fingerprints on the glass with those of your friends. Is there a match? Who is the criminal?

WHAT'S GOING ON?

Your fingerprints are unique; they are therefore a good way to identify you. When a person touches an object, a small amount of perspiration and oil from the skin's surface is transferred to the object. Powder sticks to the perspiration and oil and helps to make the prints visible.

WHAT ELSE YOU CAN DO

To keep a fingerprint that you have found, press a piece of clear tape over it. Peel off the tape and check to see that the fingerprint is on it. This is called "lifting" a print. Stick the tape onto shiny black paper.

CALGARY RAINFOREST ACTION GROUP (CRAG)

WHO WE ARE
Our main objective is education about the rainforests of the world.

Calgary Rainforest Action Group
Box, 23069, Connaught Postal Outlet
Calgary, Alberta T2S 3B1

Tel: (403) 217-1055
Fax: (403) 217-1055
E-mail: crag@Freenet.ab.ca

Meeting Place and Time
The Old Y Centre, 223-12 Ave S.W., the second Tuesday of every month from September through June, at 7:00 p.m. (call to confirm).

Membership Fees
Individual $25.00/year, family $35.00/year, student, senior, or low income $10.00/year.

WHAT WE DO
Through monthly meetings (which are free and open to the public), public lectures, films and presentations to school children, we attempt to raise the public's awareness of rainforest destruction and what can be done to stop it. School presentations have been developed for the tropical and temperate rainforest ecosystems and for the Boreal forest ecosystem.

Programs Offered
Preschool, elementary, junior and senior high school, and community.

Resources
Books, newsletters, teacher kits, speakers, presentations, slide shows/videos/films, information sheets, portable exhibits.

Facilities
Exhibits, classroom, community centre, occasional field trips.

BUILDING A RAINFOREST TREE

WHAT YOU NEED
- Dry spaghetti
- Miniature or regular-sized marshmallows

WHAT TO DO
1. Starting with one marshmallow as a base, poke several spaghetti noodles into it so that they look like spokes of a wheel. These will be the tree's roots.

2. Now add a trunk by poking another noodle into the marshmallow. How stable is your tree? Does it wobble?

3. Try adding branches to your tree by attaching another marshmallow at the top of your trunk and broken, short noodles as branches. How stable is your tree now? Does it twist and bend at the lower marshmallow?

4. Take off the bottom marshmallow with its roots and push one or two additional marshmallows onto the base of the trunk and then replace the bottom marshmallow.

5. Now take long and short noodles and stick them into the new marshmallows so they act as more supports for your tree. Does your tree wobble less? Do the additional roots allow you to make the trunk taller? Find out by using additional marshmallows to anchor a second trunk segment to the top of the first trunk noodle. How tall a tree can you build in half an hour?

WHAT'S GOING ON?
Rainforest trees are unlike other trees. Because of the abundant rainfall, they do not need deep roots to probe for water. The rainfall also dissolves away any nutrients in the soil, so the roots are not useful for feeding the tree. The roots are mainly used for supporting the tree. Rainforest trees compete for sunlight, so they have to be very tall compared to the width of their trunks. In order to support the height and weight of the trunk and branches, many rainforest trees grow wide bases, called stilts or buttresses. Almost all nutrients in a rainforest are in the trees and other plants. Once the trees are cut down or burned, the poor soil can only grow one or two crops before becoming completely barren.

CALGARY SCIENCE CENTRE

WHO WE ARE
We are a unique facility with permanent and travelling hands-on science exhibits, displays and the new multi-media Dome Theatre, like none other in the world.

Calgary Science Centre
701 - 11 St. S.W.
Calgary, Alberta   T2P 2M5

Tel: (403) 221-3700
Fax: (403) 237-0186
E-mail: discover@calgaryscience.ca

WHAT WE DO
We aim to educate and excite by presenting science programs, resources and exhibitions in Calgary and throughout southern Alberta. By doing this, we hope to encourage a personal sense of discovery in people of all ages.

Programs Offered
Elementary, junior and senior high school, youth groups, adult, family, community. **Courses:** Astronomy, astrophotography and more. **Outreach:** School outreach programs include science demonstrations and our inflatable starlab planetarium. **Summer Camps:** Space Adventurers summer camps for children aged 6 to 9. Hands-on science activities that are "out of this world"!

Resources
Newsletter, speakers, information sheets.

Facilities
Exhibits, classroom, giftshop and Dome Theatre.

CARROT PUMP

WHAT YOU NEED
- A clear glass or plastic cup
- A small carrot that will fit inside the cup
- A clear plastic straw
- 4 toothpicks
- A candle
- A few drops of ink or food colouring (optional)

WHAT TO DO
1. Scoop the leafy top out of the end of the carrot, making a small hollow.
2. Cut a 5-cm piece from the plastic straw.
3. Push the piece of straw into the hollowed-out end of the carrot.
4. Light the candle and use melted candle wax to seal the outside of the straw onto the carrot.
5. Push the toothpicks into the top of the carrot, spacing them evenly.
6. Fill the cup with tap water, almost to the rim.
7. Suspend the carrot in the water, resting the toothpicks on the rim of the cup.
8. Leave for a day or two and watch what happens.

WHAT'S GOING ON?
When a carrot grows in the ground, its cells transfer the water in the ground up to the stalks and leaves above ground by a process called osmosis. You can see osmosis at work in this activity. Osmotic pressure has pushed water up into the straw. Osmotic pressure is a kind of pump for plants, helping water to move across cell walls.

WHAT ELSE YOU CAN DO
Colour the water with ink or food colouring. After the water has risen in the straw, cut the carrot in half. What do you see? Is the ink spread evenly throughout the carrot, or are there main veins? What could the other parts of the carrot be for? Are they coloured at all? Try putting limp carrot sticks in fresh water. What happens? How long does it take them to become stiff again?

41

CALGARY SCIENCE NETWORK

WHO WE ARE
We are a non-profit organization (300 volunteer scientists) dedicated to promoting science awareness.

The Calgary Science Network (CSN)
c/o Institute of Sedimentary and Petroleum Geology (ISPG)
3303 - 33rd Street N.W.
Calgary, Alberta T2N 2A7

Tel: (403) 220-4613
Fax: (403) 284-1332
E-mail: dmjkirk@acs.ucalgary.ca

Meeting Place and Time
Second Tuesday of the month, 4:30 p.m., I.S.P.G., 3303 - 33rd St. N.W., Calgary.

Membership Fees
None.

WHAT WE DO
We operate the "Science Hotline" (see p. 132), which puts scientists in contact with elementary to high school students in the classroom. The CSN also established the Calgary Consortium for Elementary Science Education (see p. 28), which now runs our successful hands-on workshops for teachers (Making Connections) where they learn engaging ways to teach scientific phenomena. We organize various activities during National Science and Technology week, including a kick-off event, pet rock clinic, mall science and essay contest. We also publish the *Calgary Science Fun Guide,* which you are currently reading!

Programs Offered
Elementary, junior and senior high school, adult, family, community, handicapped, senior citizen, teacher training.

Resources
Book (*Calgary Science Fun Guide*), teacher kits, speakers, presentations, slide shows/videos/films, portable exhibits, equipment.

BOILING WATER WITH AN ICE CUBE

Note: Adult supervision is required for this activity.

WHAT YOU NEED
- Empty baby food jar
- Kettle or hot plate to boil water
- Oven mitts
- Ice cube

WHAT TO DO
1. Boil some water.
2. Place the jar on an oven mitt to insulate it from the countertop.
3. Fill the jar two-thirds full with boiling water and seal tightly.
4. Observe the water. Does it continue to boil? How do you know?
5. Put an ice cube on top of the lid.
6. Observe the water. What happens?

WHAT'S GOING ON?
When water boils, the bubbles we see are water vapour leaving its liquid state and going into the air above the water. Air takes up less space when it is cooled. In the airtight jar, the ice cube cools the air above the just-boiled water and creates a partial vacuum. This means there is lower air pressure in the space between the water and the lid. With lower air pressure directly above the just-boiled water, some of the water will leave its liquid state to become water vapour. In other words, the water boils (even though the water is not as hot as when it first boiled).

WHAT ELSE YOU CAN DO
Can you think of other places where water boils at a temperature of less than 100°C (the normal boiling point of water)? The activity showed us that water boiling temperature varies, depending on air pressure. At sea level, water boils at 100°C. However, in Alberta, where the air pressure is lower because we are hundreds of metres above sea level, water boils at slightly below 100°C.

BE CAREFUL!
Boiling water has enough energy to cause burns! Use your oven mitts.

CALGARY WILDLIFE REHABILITATION SOCIETY (CWRS)

WHO WE ARE

The CWRS is dedicated to treating injured and orphaned wildlife. In the process, we provide motivational work for inmates and a valuable community service.

Calgary Wildlife Rehabilitation Society
P.O. Box 20202, Bow Valley
Calgary, Alberta   T2P 4L2

Tel: (403) 234-2942
Fax: (403) 234-2997

Membership Fees

$25.00 per year.

WHAT WE DO

The CWRS provides public education through displays, newsletters and presentations. For our presentations, we generally bring with us a wild animal that could not be released back into the wild. For smaller children we bring owl pellets to dissect.

Programs Offered

Preschool, elementary, junior and senior high school, community, handicapped, senior citizen.

Resources

Newsletter, speakers, presentations (free, but donations welcome), slide shows and videos, films, live animals.

DISSECTING AN OWL PELLET

WHAT YOU NEED
- Owl pellet
- Tweezers
- Magnifying glass
- Probe, tongue depressor or Popsicle stick
- Sheet of white paper
- Latex examination gloves
- Small animal bone chart

WHAT TO DO
1. Put the latex gloves on and lay out the sheet of white paper. If the owl pellet was commercially obtained and sterilized, unwrap it and soak it in water for 5 minutes to soften it. NOTE: If your pellet is "fresh" (i.e. not sterilized), you might encounter worms or maggots. This is perfectly natural, as these small scavengers are an important part of the food web.

2. Using tweezers, remove the owl pellet from the water and place it on the white paper. Use the probe to hold the pellet still while you pull and pick it apart with your tweezers. Separate the bones from the fur and other debris.

3. Use a bone chart to identify the type of animal found in the pellet and to place the bones in the correct positions. This is like putting together a puzzle. Glue the bones to a heavy card for display (see illustration).

WHAT'S GOING ON?
Owls eat mice and other small mammals and birds in one whole piece! However, the owl's gut can't process the bones of these animals. So the owl coughs up a pellet of fur, feathers and bones about 12 hours after consuming the prey. Each pellet (an oval shape about 5 cm long and 2 cm wide) usually contains an almost complete skeleton from at least one small animal or bird. Search for "fresh" owl pellets on the floor of abandoned farm buildings (get permission first!), beneath groves of tall trees or under other structures that offer owls shelter from daylight. Try not to disturb the owl.

Owl Pellet Supply
Owl pellets, kits, etc. are available from *Science Is. . .*, Tel: (403) 547-4422. CWRS can also supply owl pellets, Tel: (403) 234-2942.

CALGARY YOUTH SCIENCE FAIR SOCIETY

WHO WE ARE
The Calgary Youth Science Fair Society is a not-for-profit organization dedicated to promoting an appreciation for scientific principles and methods in the youth of Calgary and surrounding area. Society members are volunteers from the community.

Calgary Youth Science Fair Society
515 Macleod Trail S.E.
Calgary, Alberta   T2G 2L9

Tel: (403) 271-2919
Fax: (403) 225-1926
World Wide Web: http://www.cadvision.com/cyst/

Meeting Place and Time
First Wednesday of the month, Queen Elizabeth Jr. and Sr. High School. Calgary Youth Science Fair: Big Four Building (lower), Stampede Grounds. Held each Spring; call for dates.

WHAT WE DO
We focus on organizing and presenting an annual science competition to encourage the appreciation of scientific principles and methods in Calgary's youth. Together society members coordinate the smooth running of the largest regional science fair in Canada, with over 1000 students attending every year.

Programs Offered
Grades 5 and 6, junior and senior high school. **Workshops and Special Programs:** Public viewing of projects at the Science Fair on Saturday morning. Library seminars.

Resources
Information about the fair and registration material are distributed directly to schools. A complimentary information sheet is available on fair day.

Facilities during Science Fair
Student exhibits, other related exhibits, T-shirt sales, snack bar.

BUILDING A FLY TRAP

NOTE: Adult supervision is required for this activity.

WHAT YOU NEED
- Heavy scissors, sharp knife
- Sheet of bendable plastic or poster board about 30 cm x 60 cm
- String, pencil, ruler
- Duct tape
- 4 Popsicle sticks
- Clear plastic salad container about 10 cm x 20 cm
- Bait (meat or fruit)

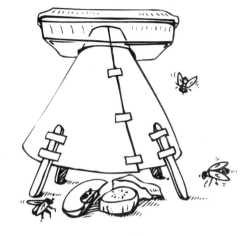

WHAT TO DO
1. Take the sheet of plastic, cut out a semicircle and form it into a cone. The bottom diameter should be about 30 cm. The top should have an opening about 2.5 cm in diameter.

2. Tape the cone together and use scissors to make the top opening even.

3. Tape four Popsicle sticks like stilts around the base of the cone, so it is raised by about 5 cm.

4. Take the salad container and sharp knife, and cut a hole about 5 cm in diameter in the flat bottom of the container.

5. Place the container on the cone so the tip of the cone comes at least half way up into the container.

6. Set some bait, such as meat or fruit, under the cone.

7. Put your fly trap in a location that normally has lots of flies.

8. Watch and wait to see what happens.

WHAT'S GOING ON?
This trap works because it is based on an interesting fact of fly behaviour: after a fly eats, it flies straight up.

WHAT ELSE YOU CAN DO
Change the conditions of the trap: type of bait; where the trap is set; time of day you set out the trap.

CALGARY ZOO, BOTANICAL GARDEN AND PREHISTORIC PARK

WHO WE ARE
We are a unique facility in Calgary, where many different types of wildlife live in captivity, but in natural habitats.

Calgary Zoo, Botanical Garden and Prehistoric Park
P.O. Box 3036, Stn. B,
Calgary, Alberta T2M 4R8

Tel: (403) 232-9386
Fax: (403) 261-9091
E-mail: www.calgaryzoo.ab.ca

Admission Fees
Adult(18–64)/ Seniors (65+) $8.00 October to April, $9.50 May to September; Seniors (Tuesdays to Thursdays) $4.00 October to April, $4.75 May to September; Children (2–17) $4.00 October to April, $4.75 May to September; under 2–free.

Days and Hours
Open every day of the year 9:00 a.m. to 4:00 p.m. Extended hours (until 6:00 p.m.), every day mid June to Labour Day weekend, and weekends from Easter to mid June and Labour Day to Thanksgiving.

WHAT WE DO
We aim to develop an awareness, enjoyment, understanding, and appreciation of the natural world while contributing to Calgarians' and visitors' well-being.

Programs Offered
Tours: School groups or corporate clients. Short interpretive programs, "Nature Tales", for the public, May to August. **Special Programs:** Presentations, hikes, activities: Safari Sleepovers, craft classes, special occasion events. Call for details. **Outreach**: Mini Zoos—for those unable to visit the zoo (e.g., hospital and nursing home patients), school programs, slide presentations. **Summer Camps:** Week-long children's day camps: *Discover the Zoo* (completed Grades 1 to 3); *Junior Zoologists* (completed Grades 4 to 6).

Resources
Memberships, member's newsletter *What's New at the Zoo*.

CREATING A BETTER SCAVENGER

WHAT YOU NEED
- Collection of household items (e.g., toothpicks, string, wire, elastic bands, glue, tape, stirring sticks)
- Scavenger food challenge materials (e.g., raw eggs, small Styrofoam ball in a cup, plastic bag with 4 kg of sand, dry leaves, bowl of wet noodles covered with plastic wrap, popcorn kernels, tapioca, rice)

WHAT TO DO
1. Think about the animals that scavenge things in your area. How do crows and ravens eat "road kill"? How do coyotes feed off a carcass? Think about how scavengers eat something that is already dead.

2. Set up three (or more if you like) of the following scavenging simulations, using the scavenger "food":
   - carcass or food scrap to pick up (e.g., bag filled with sand or leaves)
   - carcass with meat and organs (e.g., covered bowl of noodles)
   - carcass to be hidden underground for a later feast
   - fragile food morsel to be carried to safety
   - slippery, oil-rich fish eggs to be picked up and eaten

3. Using the household items, create "animal" body parts that will be able to perform scavenging tasks.

4. Test the "body parts" on make-believe carcasses and food items. Try testing different food items and body parts.

5. Note the body parts that worked best. Why were they useful? What real animal body parts do they compare to? Think about your favourite and least favourite animals. What body adaptations do they have for survival?

WHAT'S GOING ON?
By trying out different body adaptations, you can figure out how bio-mechanics works for scavengers. Bio-mechanics is the study of energy and forces and their effect on living bodies. The more efficient the bio-mechanics, the easier it is for a scavenger to get its next meal.

CANADIAN ABORIGINAL SCIENCE AND TECHNOLOGY SOCIETY (CASTS)

WHO WE ARE

We are a society seeking to promote science among Aboriginal youths and to develop technologically informed leaders within the Aboriginal community.

Canadian Aboriginal Science and Technology Society
310-6940 Fisher Road, S.E.
Calgary, Alberta   T2H 0W3

Tel: (403) 258-1775
Fax: (403) 258-1811
World Wide Web: www.Treaty7.org (click on "Friends of Treaty 7")

Membership Fees

Varied, based on type of membership.

WHAT WE DO

C.A.S.T.S. acts as a catalyst for the advancement of Canadian Aboriginal people as they seek to become self-reliant and self-determined members of society. The overall goals of C.A.S.T.S. are: (1) to increase Aboriginal involvement in science and technology fields; (2) to enhance the quality of life for Aboriginal people; (3) to identify and secure a supportive network in the promotion of science and technology; and (4) to promote ongoing professional development of resources (i.e., financial, human, and technological).

Programs Offered

Elementary, junior and senior high school, post-secondary credit, teacher training, adult, family, community, handicapped, senior citizen, youth groups.

Resources

Memberships. Scholarships are available for post-secondary aboriginal students.

CRICKET THERMOMETER

WHAT YOU NEED

- Timepiece (wristwatch, stopwatch) that indicates seconds
- Calculator

WHAT TO DO

1. On a summer evening, listen for the chirps of crickets.

2. Try to isolate the chirp of one cricket.

3. Looking at your timepiece, count the number of chirps in 14 seconds.

4. Add 40 to that number and the result will be close to the temperature in degrees Fahrenheit (°F).

5. To find the temperature in degrees Celsius (°C), subtract 32 from the Fahrenheit number, and multiply by five-ninths.

WHAT'S GOING ON?

Insects, like other cold-blooded animals, can move more rapidly in warm weather than in cold, when they are sluggish. Crickets chirp more rapidly as the temperature goes up. Honey bees are so temperature-sensitive that they stay inside their hives when the outside temperature is below 12°C. If you see a bee flying on a winter's day, you'll know that the temperature is at least 12°C.

CANADIAN CANCER SOCIETY - CALGARY UNIT

WHO WE ARE
We are a Canada-wide society with a chapter in Calgary dedicated to increasing public awareness about cancer, and to raising funds for cancer research.

Canadian Cancer Society
2nd Floor, 215 - 12 Avenue S.E.
Calgary, Alberta

Tel: (403) 205-3966
Fax: (403) 205-3979

WHAT WE DO
We offer educational resources that focus on cancer prevention and early detection.

Programs Offered
Preschool, elementary, junior and senior high school, adult, family, community, youth groups.

Resources
Newsletter, teaching kits, speakers, presentations, videos, information sheets, pamphlets, posters.

Facilities
Library.

IT'S A-PEELING!

WHAT YOU NEED

- Variety of fruit (grapes, apples, oranges, bananas)—two of each type
- Sunscreens with different SPFs
- Cookie sheet
- Paring knife

WHAT TO DO

1. Peel one of each type of fruit.
2. Place all fruit on a cookie sheet.
3. Place cookie sheet in the hot sun for a few hours and leave it undisturbed.
4. Bring the fruit in and carefully remove the peel from the rest of the fruit.
5. Compare it to the fruit that had the peel removed before being placed in the sun. Which looks more healthy and attractive? Is peel important for protecting what's underneath it?

WHAT'S GOING ON?

The fruit with its peel (skin) removed quickly browned or dehydrated in the hot sun. The fruit with its skin intact was fine, even after sitting in the sun for a while. Skin is vital for keeping things healthy. It protects us from disease, regulates our body temperature, and much more, even though it is often taken for granted. We all love a hot, sunny day, but too much of a good thing can be bad! A small amount of sunlight will cause skin cells to tan, but too much sun causes redness, pain and swelling. Over time, exposure to sunlight can result in skin cancer. It is important to protect your skin from the sun's ultraviolet radiation by using high SPF sunscreen whenever you are outside for a long time. Protect your skin because it protects the rest of you!

WHAT ELSE YOU CAN DO

Try different sunscreens on the exposed fruit. Do they protect the tissue?

BE CAREFUL!

Make sure an adult helps if you use a knife to remove the skin. With most fruit, however, you can simply peel the skin off.

CANADIAN DIABETES ASSOCIATION

WHO WE ARE
We are a Canada-wide association dedicated to increasing public awareness about diabetes.

Canadian Diabetes Association - Calgary and District Branch
114, 1212 - 1st St. S.E.
Calgary, Alberta T2G 0G8

Tel: (403) 266-0620
Fax: (403) 269-8927
E-mail: almorg@diabetes.ca

Membership Fees
Regular - $20.00
Senior - $12.00

WHAT WE DO
We have educational symposiums, fundraising events, support groups, referral information, and have literature—free pamphlets and books for sale.

Programs Offered
Educational presentations for elementary, junior and senior high schools, adults, families, communities and senior citizens.

Resources
Books, newsletter, speakers, presentations, magazines, information sheets, portable exhibits.

MOUTH MAGIC
(Making Starch Turn to Sugar)

WHAT YOU NEED
- 1 raw, fresh potato (make sure it's not green)
- Paring knife
- Tongue chart

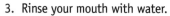

WHAT TO DO
1. Cut a "french-fry" sized slice of raw potato.
2. Using the tongue chart, place the "fry" on different locations (sides, back, front) and observe what you taste in each location.
3. Rinse your mouth with water.
4. Thoroughly moisten the tip of the "fry" with saliva and wait for one minute.
5. Place the tip of the "fry" on the side, back and front of the tongue. Do you notice any difference?

WHAT'S GOING ON?
Potatoes are made up largely of starch. The raw potato will have a slightly bitter taste that will be detected by the taste buds at the back of the tongue. Saliva contains an enzyme that changes starch into sugar. That is why when you chew starchy foods such as bread or potatoes, they begin to taste more sweet. When you "soak" the end of the potato in saliva and let it sit long enough for the chemical reaction to occur, it will contain enough sugar to have a sweet taste. The sweet taste is more readily detected by the taste buds at the front of the tongue.

Diabetics must carefully control the amount of sugar they ingest, so it's important for them to also control the amount of starch that they eat, because it's converted to sugar.

CANADIAN LIVER FOUNDATION

WHO WE ARE

We are a Canada-wide foundation devoted exclusively to providing support for research and education into the causes, diagnosis, prevention and treatment of liver disease.

Canadian Liver Foundation
1324B Centre Street North
Calgary, Alberta

Tel: (403) 276-3390
Fax: (403) 276-3423
E-mail: clf@liver.ca
World Wide Web: http://www.liver.ca

Membership Fees

Individual - $30.00/year, Seniors - $15.00/year, Organizations - $50.00/year.

WHAT WE DO

Special events: March—Help Fight Liver Disease month—sell daisies; June—Golf tournament; November—Luge for Liver. We also go to elementary schools with a video *Love Your Liver*. We go into high schools with a video *Hep.'B'—B Aware B Warned"*.

Programs Offered

Elementary, junior and senior high school, youth groups, adult, family, teacher training.

Resources

Newsletter, teacher kits, speakers, presentations, videos, information sheets, portable exhibits.

Facilities

Office meeting room. Library.

SLOW DE-LI-VER-Y

WHAT YOU NEED
- 2 coffee filters
- 2 funnels
- 2 glasses
- A few drops red food colouring
- 250 mL water
- 15 mL margarine

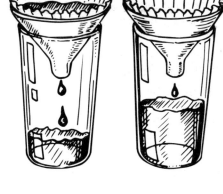

WHAT TO DO
1. On the inside of one of the coffee filters, rub the margarine evenly over the bottom and about 2 cm up the sides.
2. Place the ungreased coffee filter in one of the funnels and the greased coffee filter in the other funnel. Be sure that the filter paper fills the funnel so that there is nowhere for liquid to escape.
3. Place one funnel on top of each glass.
4. Add a few drops of red food colouring to 250 mL of water. Pour 125 mL of the water into one funnel and 125 mL of the water into the other funnel.
5. Leave for about one hour and observe what happens.

WHAT'S GOING ON?
This experiment demonstrates what happens to a liver that is not functioning properly. Did you find that the ungreased filter let the water go right through, while the greased filter prevented this from happening? The red coloured water represents blood, the greased filter paper represents an unhealthy, clogged liver and the plain filter paper represents a healthy liver.

The liver is the body's largest organ and does a very important job for us. A large blood vessel carries blood containing all of the food and drug material from our digestive tract to the liver. When the blood reaches the liver, it acts like a filter and a processing plant. It removes poisons from our blood, turns sugar into usable glucose for our muscles, changes fat into useful products, and rebuilds protein. If the liver is damaged, it becomes clogged and cannot act as a proper filter for blood.

CANADIAN PARKS AND WILDERNESS SOCIETY CALGARY/BANFF CHAPTER (CPAWS)

WHO WE ARE

We are a society that aims to educate students in Calgary and area about ecology, wildlife, conservation, and the connection between human needs and the need for protected areas.

Canadian Parks and Wilderness Society (Calgary/Banff Chapter)
Education Program
911 Larch Place
Canmore, Alberta   T1W 1S5

Tel/Fax: (403) 678-0079
E-mail: cpaws_education@telusplanet.net

WHAT WE DO

The Canadian Parks and Wilderness Society offers a large range of education programs to Calgary schools, including assembly presentations, in-class speakers, teacher workshops, and field trips to natural areas.

Programs Offered

CPAWS education programs promote stewardship of our natural heritage through awareness, direct experience, appreciation, and understanding. Topics include basic ecology, endangered species, biodiversity and ecosystem management, and wilderness appreciation. A variety of programs exist and can be customized to your needs.

Resources

Teacher kits, speakers, presentations, slide shows, videos, films, information sheets. Of special interest are outdoor field studies in school yards, nearby park areas or in the mountains.

BUILDING YOUR OWN WATERSHED

WHAT YOU NEED

- Regular-size shoebox with removable lid
- 20 small, blue, see-through plastic or glass beads
- 20, 10-cm pieces of fishing line
- Small stones, pine cones
- Plasticine, play dough or felt pieces (blue, green, brown)
- Construction paper (green, brown)
- Glue, scissors
- Glow-in-the-dark star, or stickers

WHAT TO DO

1. Cut out two round holes (the size of a dollar coin), side by side, in one of the short sides of the box.

2. Put the lid on the box and punch holes (at least 60) in it with the pencil.

3. Tie a blue bead at the end of each fishing line, loop the other end through two holes in the lid and tie off on the inside of the lid.

4. Create a lake (use Plasticine, felt, paper, or draw one) at the bottom of your box. Have a river flowing out of it and rocks on the shore to make a dam. Glue cones to create a forest. Make trees and animals with Plasticine.

5. Out of construction paper, cut out mountains and glue them to the inside sides of the box; stick stars above the mountains.

6. Put the lid on and look inside!

WHAT'S GOING ON?

The forests, people, the fish, the water, and wildlife are all connected through our watersheds. You have created a model of a watershed. As the rain falls on the land, it collects in a man-made lake called a "reservoir". From here, underground pipes carry water to your home. This is where your drinking water comes from. The forest is an important part of the watershed; it filters the air and the water and provides homes for the animals. Forests give us many things to make our environment healthy. We can also make many things from trees.

CANADIAN WESTERN NATURAL GAS - BLUE FLAME KITCHEN

WHO WE ARE
We are a department of Canadian Western Natural Gas. We were established in 1929 to promote the use of natural gas as a home cooking fuel.

Canadian Western Natural Gas - Blue Flame Kitchen
909 - 11 Avenue S.W.
Calgary, Alberta T2R 1L8

Tel: (403) 245-7731
Fax: (403) 245-7060

Days and Hours
Consumer Phone Line - Monday to Friday 10:30 a.m. to 4:30 p.m.

WHAT WE DO
The Blue Flame Kitchen home economists test recipes using both natural gas ranges and natural gas barbeques. All recipes are tested for Calgary's high altitude which can range from 1000 to 1200 metres above sea level.

Programs Offered
A consumer phone line is available to answer questions about cooking and baking, stain removal and food safety. A home economist will speak to groups. Barbeque and Christmas food demonstrations are held for the public every spring and fall.

Resources
A newsletter *"What's Cooking?"* is mailed three times a year. Included in each mailing are monthly recipe sheets. Home Economists also produce a yearly cookbook that includes a special section called *"Family Corner"*.

KITCHEN SCIENCE

WHAT YOU NEED

- 1 or more of: apple, pear, peach, or banana
- 1 lemon
- 2 bowls
- 1 spoon
- peeler, knife

WHAT TO DO

1. Peel and slice up all the fruit, except the lemon.
2. Divide the fruit into two bowls.
3. Squeeze the juice from the lemon and pour over the fruit in one of the bowls. With a spoon, toss the fruit until it is all covered with lemon juice.
4. Leave the fruit in the other bowl plain.
5. Wait a few hours and describe what you see.

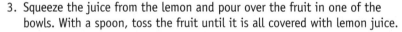

WHAT'S GOING ON?

The sliced fruit will turn brown after several hours if allowed to mix with the oxygen in the air. The lemon juice added to the fruit in the other bowl is a weak acid called citric acid. It slows down this browning process. Lemon juice, vitamin C and vinegar—substances that slow down the browning process described above—are called antioxidants.

WHAT ELSE YOU CAN DO

Vitamin C can also be used to keep the fruit fresh in appearance. Crush a vitamin C tablet between two spoons. Dissolve it in 200 mL of water and toss it with the fruit until the fruit is covered. Observe what happens after a few hours.

CHEVRON OPEN MINDS SCHOOL PROGRAM

WHO WE ARE

Our school program gives Calgary teachers the opportunity to move their classroom to the Calgary Zoo, Glenbow or the Calgary Science Centre for an entire week. Almost every week in Calgary there are students going to "school" where they may feed a hippo, make an electric motor or read diaries from the last century. What a great way to learn!

Our program is primarily funded by Chevron Canada Resources. The program is supported and fully endorsed by the Calgary Board of Education and the Calgary Roman Catholic Separate School District. Independent schools are also encouraged to apply.

Chevron Open Minds School Program
Room 216, Viscount Bennett Centre
2519 Richmond Road S.W.
Calgary, Alberta   T3E 4M2

Tel: (403) 294-8762
Fax: (403) 294-6301
E-mail: gkydd@cbe.ab.ca

WHAT WE DO

Each site has a coordinator who helps the teacher access various resources and experts. Teachers apply to the program each spring for the following school year. They attend several meetings where they are assisted in their planning by education and site staff. The teachers design and implement a long-term study that uses the week at the site as a catalyst. The program is open to teachers from Grades 1 to 12.

The intent is to give students time to become immersed in interesting experiences and to work alongside artists, scientists, inventors and other professionals. Their learning is deeper and they practice basic skills in a more meaningful context. Math makes more sense if you're measuring the polar bear enclosure!

Programs Offered

Elementary, junior and senior high school.

Resources

Presentations, slide shows, videos, films.

SPHERES OF OIL

Note: Adult supervision is required for this activity.

WHAT YOU NEED

- 125 mL water
- Clear drinking glass
- 125 mL rubbing alcohol
- Eyedropper
- Cooking oil

WHAT TO DO

1. Pour water into the glass (you can add food colouring to tint the water).
2. Tilt the glass and pour the alcohol very slowly into the water.
3. Fill the eyedropper with oil.
4. Place the tip of the dropper below the surface of the top alcohol layer and squeeze out several drops of oil.

WHAT'S GOING ON?

The alcohol forms a layer on top of the water. The drops of oil form nearly perfect spheres that float in the centre below the top of the alcohol layer that rests on top of the water layer. The downward pull of gravity has little effect on the drops of oil because they are surrounded by liquid molecules that are pulling on them in all directions. The oil drops are also pulling on each other and, without the effects of gravity, the oil pulls itself into the shape that takes up the least surface area—a sphere.

BE CAREFUL!

Rubbing alcohol is poisonous! Return it to a safe place. It is also flammable. (can catch on fire), so keep it away from flames.

THE CITY OF CALGARY, ENGINEERING AND ENVIRONMENTAL SERVICES DEPARTMENT

WHO WE ARE
We are a City of Calgary department that is involved in collecting household refuse and recyclable domestic and industrial materials.

The City of Calgary
Engineering and Environmental Services Dept.
P.O. Box 2100, Station M
Calgary Alberta T2P 2M5

Tel: (403) 277-7770 (Recycling Hotline)
Fax: (403) 276-7292
E-mail: bgoemans@gov.calgary.ab.ca

WHAT WE DO
The City of Calgary operates a residential recycling program comprising several depots where glass, cans, newspaper, magazines, catalogues, mixed paper and corrugated cardboard may be dropped off. We provide school tours of the facilities. We also prepare in-class presentations in conjunction with other Calgary area environmental groups, like "Just Imagine" —a non-profit environmental education society.

Resources
Pamphlets on recycling, composting, domestic hazardous waste; presentations; speakers; Recycling Hotline.

CREATING YOUR OWN PAPER

WHAT YOU NEED

- Two fine screens (20 cm x 20 cm) in wooden frames
- Construction paper (any colour) and white paper
- Plastic tub approximately 60 cm x 50 cm
- Blender
- Good sponge
- Cornstarch (60 mL per tub)

WHAT TO DO

1. Rip the paper into small pieces (3-5 cm) for the blender.
2. Add water to the blender (three-quarters full), then add the paper.
3. Turn the blender on for approximately 40 seconds to make pulp.
4. Fill the tub with water (three-quarters full).
5. Put the pulp from the blender in the tub.
6. Using the pulpy water in the tub, continue to make more pulp in the blender until the pulp solution is thick (approximately six to seven mixes).
7. Using one of the screens, slowly screen out the pulp.
8. Place the second screen over the pulp in the first screen, and sponge or towel it dry.
9. The pulp should be like paper. Remove it and let it dry.

WHAT'S GOING ON?

It is important to remember that paper comes from trees, which are a precious and limited resource. Fortunately, paper is easily recycled, which is what you did in this actvity. You have removed the original paper (wood) fibres from the used sheets, and then reformed them into usuable paper again. If you use a magnifier, you can actually see the tiny wood fibres and feel their texture with your fingers. The fibres from which paper is made can be recycled into many other things, including boxes, wallboard, and even tissue for your nose! Most importantly, for every tonne of paper that is recycled, you save 17 trees!

WHAT ELSE YOU CAN DO?

Try making different colours of paper, or adding sparkles to it for gift wrap.

CLEAN CALGARY ASSOCIATION

WHO WE ARE
We are a non-profit organization whose mission is to assist Calgarians develop an environmentally friendly lifestyle in a positive, proactive manner.

Clean Calgary Association
100, 3811 Edmonton Trail N.E.
Calgary, Alberta   T2E 3P5

Tel: (403) 230-1443
Fax: (403) 230-1458
E-mail: cleancal@cadvision.com

Days and Hours
Tuesday to Saturday 10:00 a.m. to 4:00 p.m.

WHAT WE DO
We provide educational programs for Calgarians interested in having an environmentally friendly lifestyle.

Programs Offered
Elementary, junior and senior high school, adult, youth groups. **Workshops and Special Programs:** WINShop - *Waste It Not* - is full of creative ideas for reusing material. It sells usable discards from local manufacturers at minimal cost.

Resources
Newsletter, teacher kits, speakers, presentations, information sheets, memberships, portable exhibits, *Teacher's Environmental Resource Manual*.

Facilities
Exhibits/displays, library.

SUNCATCHERS AND LIGHT

WHAT YOU NEED

- Clean, recycled Styrofoam trays
- Clear plastic transparency material
- Markers
- Glue or tape, string or yarn
- Scissors, sharp pencil, small cookie cutters

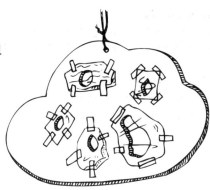

WHAT TO DO

1. Cut the edges off a Styrofoam tray so you have a flat surface.

2. Create openings in the tray with small cookie cutters, or by poking holes in a design shape using a sharp pencil.

3. Cut pieces of transparency material large enough to cover the openings, and colour the transparency pieces with markers.

4. Decide where you want to put the colours, and tape or glue the transparent material behind the openings in the tray.

5. Punch a hole near the top of the suncatcher and put a string or piece of yarn through and knot it.

6. Hang the suncatcher in a sunny spot or attach it to the window.

WHAT'S GOING ON?

White light from the sun is made up of different colours. When you look at a rainbow, you can see white sunlight broken up into a beautiful colour spectrum of red, orange, yellow, green, blue, indigo and violet. By using a filter like the pieces of coloured transparency that you cut, you can take colours out of white light. Filters allow only light of the same colour to pass through them. If you coloured your transparency blue, then only the blue part of white light can go through it. All the other colours are absorbed by the filter. This is how we see colours. When you look at a bright red rose, it is absorbing all of the colours from the sun **except** for red, which bounces off and reaches our eyes. In the evening, as sunlight fades, we see fewer and fewer colours.

WHAT ELSE YOU CAN DO

Put different coloured transparencies over the top of an existing one and discover what new colours are formed.

COAL ASSOCIATION OF CANADA

WHO WE ARE
We are an industry association representing Canadian coal producers, users and shippers.

The Coal Association of Canada
502, 205 - 9th Avenue S.E.
Calgary, Alberta T2G 0R3

Tel: (403) 262-1544
Fax: (403) 265-7604
Toll Free: 1-800-910-2625
E-mail: jimwood@agt.net
World Wide Web: http://www.coal.ca

Membership Fees
Call for details.

Meeting Place and Time
Call for details.

WHAT WE DO
We represent Canadian coal producers. The value of Canada's coal production contributes over $5.8 billion per year to the Canadian economy. Coal is the single largest commodity carried by Canadian railways and is exported to over 20 countries on five continents.

Programs Offered
Elementary and junior high school.

Resources
Teacher kits, information sheets, publications.

Facilities
Library.

MAKING A COAL FLOWER GARDEN

WHAT YOU NEED

- 90 mL salt
- 90 mL liquid blueing
- 15 mL ammonia
- An old pan
- Vaseline
- Pieces of coal or charcoal briquettes
- Food colouring

WHAT TO DO

1. Find an old pan and grease the edges with Vaseline (this prevents the mixture from going over the edge).
2. Place a few pieces of coal or charcoal briquettes in the pan.
3. Mix the salt, liquid blueing and ammonia together.
4. Pour the salt mixture over the coal.
5. Dab drops of food colouring on top of the coal (you can use a variety of colours).
6. Watch your garden grow. Be patient! You should start to see crystals by the next day.

WHAT'S GOING ON?

The crystals are formed by salt molecules joining together as the liquid evaporates into the air. The ammonia helps to speed up the rate of evaporation.

WHAT ELSE YOU CAN DO

You can grow crystals of rock candy by dissolving sugar in hot water. Pour the hot sugar water into a glass and dangle a piece of string from a pencil into the liquid. As the liquid cools, sugar crystals appear on the string.

BE CAREFUL!

If you are making the sugar crystals, be sure to get an adult to help, as hot water can be dangerous.

COCHRANE ECOLOGICAL INSTITUTE

WHO WE ARE
The Cochrane Ecological Institute includes a wildlife sanctuary of 160 acres of rolling, mixed woodland, wetland, and prairie set in the foothills of the Rockies. Students from all over the world use our location as a field station for research into ways to preserve our world's dwindling natural heritage.

Cochrane Ecological Institute
P.O. Box 484
Cochrane, Alberta TOL 0W0

Tel: (403) 932-5632
Fax: (403) 932-6303
E-mail: cei@cadvision.com
World Wide Web: cuug.ab.ca:8001/~scholefp/swiftfox.html

Days and Hours
Injured wildlife received 24 hours. Guided tours by appointment only.

Admission Fees
$10.00 each tour. Workshops and summer camps—call for prices.

WHAT WE DO
We breed endangered indigenous animals for reintroduction and have developed non intrusive survey methods. We provide education programs on the rehabilitation and release of injured and orphaned wildlife.

Programs Offered
Programs for all ages. **Tours:** Summer science camps—wildlife workshops. Guided tours of field station used for research into indigenous flora and fauna. **Workshops and Special Programs:** Each week from July to November, workshops on wildlife, environmental philosophy, ethics, art, and music. **Outreach:** Talks on swift fox and indigenous species, flora and fauna—with slides, sound, reading lists. **Summer Camps:** For children aged 6 to 11.

Resources
Books, newsletter, presentations, videos, films, info sheets, portable exhibits.

Facilities
Auditorium, exhibits, interpretive centre, library, live animals, bookstore, giftshop, cafeteria, snack bar.

WONDROUS MINI-WORLDS

WHAT YOU NEED
- Plastic ice-cream pail lid or Frisbee
- Magnifying glass
- Notebook and pencil

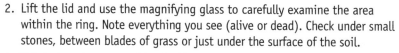

WHAT TO DO
1. In your backyard, or in a park or forest, place the ice-cream pail lid, or the Frisbee, top side up on the ground. Gently push down to form an outline ring.

2. Lift the lid and use the magnifying glass to carefully examine the area within the ring. Note everything you see (alive or dead). Check under small stones, between blades of grass or just under the surface of the soil.

3. Think about how everything inside your ring is related. Do the insects depend on the plants? Are some of the insects predators of others? How are the insects and plants adapted to this particular environment? If there is garbage, how does that affect the rest of the environment?

WHAT'S GOING ON?
What you are looking at is a "mini" ecosystem. An ecosystem is all the living and non-living things in a particular place. Scientists study large ecosystems, to learn more about nature and environments and how to protect them. Even a tiny part of a larger ecosystem can tell us a lot about the health of the environment. Remember, every single thing (living or dead) in an ecosystem affects every other thing. So, if there's a problem with one part, the entire ecosystem is affected. Ecosystems affect each other too, so everything on Earth is therefore connected. Because of this, we must make sure that we do everything we can to protect every ecosystem, no matter how small!

WHAT ELSE YOU CAN DO
When you've finished at one location, go to another and repeat Steps 1 and 2. How do the environments compare? Leave the lid or Frisbee on the ground overnight, then look under it. What's changed? You've created a new ecosystem!

BE CAREFUL!
Whenever you are dealing with unknown organisms, it's best not to touch them. They prefer it that way, too!

ENERGEUM

WHO WE ARE

The Energeum is Alberta's liveliest energy visitor centre. It is operated by the Alberta Energy and Utilities Board (EUB), which regulates all aspects of the energy industry in the province of Alberta.

Energeum - EUB
640 - 5 Avenue S.W.
Calgary, Alberta   T2P 3G4

Tel: (403) 297-4293
Fax: (403) 297-3757
World Wide Web: http://www.eub.gov.ab.ca

Admission Fees

Free.

Days and Hours

Monday to Friday, 10:30 a.m. to 4:30 p.m.; open Sundays and holidays in June, July and August.

WHAT WE DO

We enable visitors to experience the story of Alberta's energy resources (oil, oil sands, natural gas, coal, electricity, and alternate energy) with hands-on displays, computer games and working models.

Programs Offered

Tours: Guided tours for all ages. Group talks about history, development and use of Alberta's energy resources. Special events with activities on most holidays.
Special Programs: Hands-on, curriculum-based programs for Grades 2 to 12 and post-secondary level about all aspects of Alberta's energy resources. $2.00 per student, supervisors free. **Outreach:** Some offsite programs given. Teachers' kits for loan or rent for classroom use. **Summer Day Camps:** Two-hour, fun-filled, hands-on programs. Book in July and August, especially for ages 5 to 12.

Resources

Teacher kits, presentations, slide shows, videos, brochures, information sheets.

Facilities

Small theatre, interpretive centre with exhibits and hands-on displays, library (on 2nd floor), cafeteria/snack bar (on 10th floor).

NEVER FAIL MAGNETIC NAIL

WHAT YOU NEED
- 1 **iron** nail
- 6-volt battery
- 3 m of thin coated copper wire
- 5-10 metal paper clips

WHAT TO DO
1. Find the middle of the length of wire. This is where you will start winding your wire around the nail. From the middle, continue winding around the nail until there is about 50 cm of wire left unwound on each end.

2. Strip plastic coating from the ends of the wire (approximately 2 cm). Make a hook shape with the exposed copper.

3. Attach one of the ends to one battery terminal. Try and pick up a paper clip. Were you able to?

4. Now attach the other end of the wire to the other terminal and try to pick up a paper clip again. What happened this time?

WHAT'S GOING ON?
The chemical energy inside the battery is being converted into magnetic energy. When you complete the electric circuit attaching the wire ends to both battery terminals, the current moving through the wire creates a magnetic field. This causes the iron nail to act like a magnet until the circuit is broken by disconnecting one of the terminals.

WHAT ELSE YOU CAN DO
Experiment to see how the number of wire coils around the nail affects the strength of the magnet. Try batteries with different voltages to see how that affects the strength of the magnet.

BE CAREFUL!
Be sure to have an adult supervise you during this activity. Remind them that a battery is a safe power source but an electrical outlet is not! Be sure to detach the wire from the battery terminals when you're done. If you don't, the energy from the battery is converted to heat energy and the wire gets very hot!

ENVIRONMENTAL PROTECTION - NATURAL RESOURCES SERVICE FISH AND WILDLIFE

WHO WE ARE
We are a provincial government department that promotes sustainable, safe recreational use of Alberta's wildlife and natural habitats.

Environmental Protection - Natural Resources Service Fish and Wildlife
100, 3115 - 12 St. N.E.
Calgary, Alberta T2E 7J2

Tel: (403) 297-6423
Fax: (403) 297-2843
World Wide Web Sites:
Amphibians: http://www.gov.ab.cal ~env/nrs/wildlife/amphib/index.html

Threatened Wildlife: http://www.gov.ab.ca/~env/nrs/wildlife/threatsp/ index.html

Fish: http://www.gov.ab.ca/~env/nrs/wmd/ fishing/gamefish.html

Upland Game Birds/Ducks and Geese/Big Game Animals:
http://www.gov.ab.ca/~env/nrs/wmd/ hunting/index.html

Federal Government-Canadian Wildlife Service: http://www.doe.ca/envcan (Click on language of your choice to reach Hinterland Who's Who).

WHAT WE DO
We enforce hunting and fishing regulations to ensure wildlife is properly managed.

Programs Offered
Elementary, junior high school. Our hunter education programs have a hands-on kit that includes samples of different animal furs for children to feel.

Resources
Speakers (limited), presentations. We have two work books for children: one on animals and one on fish. Our resource material on Alberta animals includes a poster on different animals, which shows where they are in the food chain relative to man. We also have information booklets on bears, wolves and bats, and information on Alberta upland game birds.

A FISHY STORY

WHAT YOU NEED
- Aquarium with goldfish
- Pencil and paper

WHAT TO DO
1. Review the names of the fins at different locations on a goldfish's body.

adipose fin (not goldfish)

dorsal fin

tail fin (caudal fin)

anal fin

pelvic fins

pectoral fins

2. Observe the goldfish for several minutes. Which fin(s) do you think the fish uses for propulsion? What observations lead you to think this? Which fin(s) do you think the fish uses for turning? What observations lead you to think this?

3. Draw a table with one column for each of the five types of fins on a goldfish. Observe again for several minutes.

4. Record one X in the correct column each time you observe the movement of a fin. Count up your X's in each column to see which fin(s) the goldfish uses most.

WHATS GOING ON?
Observation is a skill important to any scientist or budding scientist. Detailed recording, such as by using a table, is important to help you make sense of what you see. You may have recorded, for instance, that the tail fin moved the most. The goldfish uses the tail fin for two important actions: for propulsion and for changing direction. The pairs of pelvic and pectoral fins also help the fish steer and balance in the water. The dorsal and anal fins act like keels to stabilize the fish in the water. Not all fish have the same fins as a goldfish. There are 49 different species of Alberta fish. The diagram shows a dotted line where some fish (such as trout) have an adipose fin. Other Alberta fish, like the walleye, have a double dorsal fin or other differences in their fins. Next time you are at the grocery store, look at a whole trout, and observe its fins. How do they differ from the fins of your goldfish?

Note: Goldfish are not native to Alberta lakes and streams, so please never release them into the wild.

EVERGREEN THEATRE

WHO WE ARE

We are a collective of performers, educators and scientists exploring the science of the natural world through original music and theatre.

Evergreen Theatre
304, 524 - 17 Avenue S.W.
Calgary, Alberta T2S 0B2

Tel: (403) 228-1384
Fax: (403) 229-1385

WHAT WE DO

Whether it's called entertaining education or educational entertainment, Evergreen Theatre's programs are definitely fun! The concepts explored in our shows are illustrated by examining the plants, animals, habitats, and natural processes of Alberta. With sufficient notice, the Evergreen Co-op can develop a custom program to meet your specific needs. Workshops on the use of music and theatre as instructional tools are also available.

Programs Offered

Elementary, junior and senior high school, teacher training, family, community, adult, youth groups.

Resources

Teacher kits, presentations.

BEE WAGGLE DANCE

WHAT YOU NEED
• Nothing!

WHAT TO DO
1. Practise the two basic bee dances: the round and the waggle (see illustration). The patterns are related to each other, as you can see in the illustration. Try dancing from the round into the waggle, and then back again.
2. Try the dances in a small space, then over a larger area. Is it more difficult to repeat the small or the large pattern?

WHAT'S GOING ON?
Bees perform the important function of pollination as they travel from flower to flower in search of nectar. Bees must make thousands of trips to flowers to make just one teaspoon of honey. Bee "dances" are a complex form of communication through which bees tell each other about the type and location of nectar supplies. If food is up to 10 m away, bees do the round dance. If food is more than 100 m away, bees do the waggle. Between 10 and 100 m, bees dance a combination of the two dances: the actual combination depending on the distance to the food. Bees also use the sun as a compass to indicate directions; they see the sun even on hazy days.

WHAT ELSE YOU CAN DO
Try group dances. Everyone forms a human chain and goes through the dance patterns together. Each person finds a partner. One partner chooses a spot as the location of some imaginary food. Then, the object is to communicate to the other person, through a bee dance, the food's location.

FEESA, AN ENVIRONMENTAL EDUCATION SOCIETY

WHO WE ARE
We are an environmental education society.

FEESA, an Environmental Education Society
601, 10179 - 105 Street
Edmonton, Alberta T5J 3N1

Southern Alberta Office
c/o Kananaskis Field Stations
186 Biosciences - University of Calgary
Calgary, Alberta T2N 1N4

Tel: (403) 421-1497
Fax: (403) 425-4506

Southern Alberta:
Tel: (403) 220-2819
Fax: (403) 220-0814

WHAT WE DO
We provide Alberta students and teachers with quality bias-balanced environmental education resources and services. **Tours:** For students—field-based or classroom "tours" of Alberta's forests. For teachers—one-, three- or eight-day, field-based professional development programs at no cost. **Workshops and Special Programs:** Classroom presentations on forest-related topics at no cost. Educator professional development on many environmental topics—full scholarships available. **Summer Camps:** Extended professional development workshops on environmental themes—travel throughout Alberta—full scholarships available to Alberta educators. Although FEESA does not have a facility, its access to a myriad of facilities and study areas makes it among the leaders in environmental education in Alberta, and the leader in promoting "bias-balanced", process-oriented education for educators and their students.

Programs Offered
Elementary, junior and senior high school, post-secondary credit, youth groups, teacher training.

Resources
Newsletter, teacher kits, speakers, slide shows, videos.

WILDLIFE SAFARI

WHAT YOU NEED
- Sheet of white paper or cloth (observation surface)
- Paper and pencil (for recording observations)
- White plastic spoon (specimen collector)
- 3 white plastic or foam cups
- Tape
- Magnifying glass
- Square of clear, stiff plastic for lid to cover cups (optional)
- Friend or adult to go on safari with

WHAT TO DO
1. Tape the three cups together so that each cup touches the sides of the other two for stability. You now have a triple observation chamber.
2. Gather the other materials together for the safari (into your backyard, a playground, a park, etc.).
3. Before starting the safari, discuss with your friend where you might find wild creatures (invertebrates, better known as bugs). The best places to look for them is where they find shelter, such as under leaves or rotting vegetation, cracks in trees, under rocks or logs, in cracks in cement or in grass clumps growing beside buildings.
4. When you find a specimen, carefully pick it up and place it either in one of the cups or on the white sheet for observation. Use your magnifying glass to look for details, such as number of legs, body parts, wings, colour, etc.
5. Draw a picture of your creature before returning it to nature.

WHAT ELSE YOU CAN DO
Compare the creatures you found by finding as many similarities and differences as you can. This is how scientists classify organisms.

BE CAREFUL!
Make sure you don't try to catch stinging insects, such as bees or wasps.

FISH CREEK PROVINCIAL PARK: FISH CREEK ENVIRONMENTAL LEARNING CENTRE AND BOW VALLEY RANCH VISITOR CENTRE

WHO WE ARE
We are part of Alberta Environmental Protection, a provincial government department. We are an environmental education centre for all students from ECS to Grade 12, as well as post-secondary.

Fish Creek Environmental Learning Centre and Bow Valley Ranch Visitor Centre
13931 Woodpath Road S.W.
Calgary, Alberta T2W 5R6

Tel: (403) 297-7827
Fax: (403) 297-7849
E-mail: jrreading@cbe.ab.ca

Hours of Admission and Rates
8:00 a.m. to 10:00 p.m., $2.00 per child per program (full day); $1.00 per child per program (half day and evenings).

WHAT WE DO
We offer curriculum-connected environmental education programs, professional development, corporate and community programs and consulting services.

Programs Offered
Tours: Twenty-five curriculum-connected programs that support science education. **Workshops and Special Programs:** One hundred workshops and professional development series throughout the school year. **Outreach:** Friends of Fish Creek have many projects that reflect park policies, mandate and objectives. **Summer Camps:** No organized summer camps, but facilities are available for groups who wish to conduct summer activities (corporations, community groups, etc.).

Resources
Books, newsletter, teacher kits, speakers, presentations, slide shows, videos, films, information sheets, portable exhibits, equipment, people to assist.

Facilities
Bow Valley Ranch *(East end of Fish Creek Provincial Park)* — auditorium, museum, exhibits. Library, outdoor teaching areas, campfire areas, amphitheatres, the natural pond environment. **Fish Creek Environmental Learning Centre** *(West end of Fish Creek Provincial Park)* — five classrooms, library, outdoor teaching areas, campfire areas.

BEAK WATCHING

WHAT YOU NEED

- Different "beaks": spoon, tweezers, clothespin, tongs
- Food samples: small and large seeds, cereal, pasta shapes, marbles, foam chips
- Stomach: sandwich bag

WHAT TO DO

1. Put the different types of food in different containers, for example:
   - seeds on a flat cookie sheet
   - marbles in a cereal bowl
   - foam chips in a bowl filled with water
   - pasta shapes on a tray
   - cereal in a shallow container filled with sand

2. Try feeding yourself by using the different "beaks" to put the food in your stomach (the sandwich bag). Keep the bag at arm's length from the food source. Try not to get any sand or water in the bags.

3. Does one kind of beak work better than another? Is one beak better for a particular kind of food? Can you think of birds in nature that have beaks like the ones you used?

WHAT'S GOING ON?

A bird's beak can tell us a lot about its way of life. Birds of prey have hooked beaks for tearing flesh (bald eagles rip salmon open; golden eagles can tear the hide of dead sheep and hares). Wading birds have long, slender bills for probing in soft mud, where they find worms. Ducks have broad, flat bills that have a sieve inside for filtering tiny seeds from mud and water. Other birds have beaks designed for cracking hard nuts.

WHAT ELSE YOU CAN DO

The next time you're in a park or by the river, go bird watching. Have a look at the birds' beaks. Try to guess what kinds of food they eat and how they gather the food.

GEOLOGICAL SURVEY OF CANADA

WHO WE ARE
We are a federal institution, part of Natural Resources Canada, dedicated to geoscience research, especially related to western and northern Canada. As one of Canada's oldest scientific research organizations (established 1842), our research has been instrumental in the exploration and development of the nation.

Geological Survey of Canada (Calgary)
3303 - 33 Street N.W.
Calgary, Alberta T2L 2A7

Tel: (403) 292-7130
Fax: (403) 292-5377
World Wide Web Sites:
http://www.nrcan.gc.ca/~rose/gsccalhp.htm (GSC Calgary)
http://www.nrcan.gc.ca/gsc/ (GSC Ottawa)
http://www.nrcan.gc.ca/gsc/cpdnew/askageol.html (Ask-a-Geologist)
http://geonames.nrcan.gc.ca/english/ (Canada's geographical names)

WHAT WE DO
Our research subjects include oil, gas, coal, and minerals; palaeontology, geochemistry, geophysics, environmental geoscience, resource assessments, and geological mapping.

Programs Offered
Outreach: The annual *Pet Rock and Fossil Clinic* , held every year in October during Science and Technology Week at GSC Calgary. Scientists visit schools through our connection with the Calgary Science Network and Science Hotline. We hold public lectures and provide classroom presentations, science curriculum assistance to teachers, and assistance in preparing and judging science fairs.

Resources
Geological reports, rock and mineral sets, information sheets, videos.

Facilities
One of western Canada's largest geoscience libraries, a bookstore (geological books and maps, and some more general items).

MOUNTAIN BUILDING

WHAT YOU NEED

- 4 different colours of Plasticine or dough coloured with food colouring (blue, green, red, yellow)
- 2 large books covered in plastic wrap

WHAT TO DO

1. Prepare four different layers of Plasticine, about 15 cm x 8 cm x 1 cm each.

2. Stack the layers on top of each other.

3. Stand the books up on opposite sides of the layers.

4. Have someone gently push on one of the books while you gently push on the other until the Plasticine folds.

5. Increase the pressure slowly until more folding occurs.

6. Draw a picture of what happened.

WHAT'S GOING ON?

Sedimentary rocks are formed from deposits of mud, silt or sand at the bottom of
the sea. The rocks form in horizontal layers much like the layers of Plasticine you constructed. Powerful forces in the Earth push on the rock layers. After millions of years have gone by, the rock layers fold, much like the Plasticine did.

The arch of the Plasticine fold represents an anticline, which could be the top of a mountain. The upside down arch of the fold, the trough, or syncline could represent a valley. Later, rivers or glaciers erode the land surface to sculpt new valleys and hillsides. Old mountains are the remnants of once larger uplifts and can contain both synclines and anitclines, as seen at Cascade Mountain near Banff. Old valleys are where the rocks were softer and easier to erode.

GIRL GUIDES OF CANADA

WHO WE ARE
We are an organization designed to encourage girls to participate in various activities that promote community service, self-awareness, and personal achievements in a group setting.

Girl Guides of Canada—Calgary Area
2188 Brownsea Drive N.W.
Calgary, Alberta   T2N 3G9

Tel: (403) 283-8348
Fax: (403) 283-9781

Meeting Place and Time
Various locations throughout the city. Contact the Guide office for specific locations for your neighborhood.

Membership Fees
Approximately $40.00-$45.00 per year.

WHAT WE DO
We provide programs for girls aged 5 to 17 that include outdoor activities, nature study, interest badges, field trips, and career opportunities. We also participate in the national *Water for Tomorrow* environmental program.

Programs Offered
Elementary, junior and senior high, adult.

Facilities
Library, bookstore and giftshop, conference/meeting rooms.

JELLY LENSES

WHAT YOU NEED

- 1 packet of lemon or other light coloured Jell-O

- Cold, hot, and boiling water

- Measuring cup, spoon, small bowl, tray, Plasticine or foil

- For lens shaping: a variety of ladles, ice cream scoops, stem glassware, round-bottom bowls

- Piece of clear plastic, plastic wrap or glass

- Newspaper

WHAT TO DO

1. Mix Jell-O and 185 mL boiling water in a bowl until the Jell-O is dissolved.

2. Set the containers for lens shaping on a tray and fill them with the Jell-O mixture.

3. Support the containers with Plasticine or foil to avoid spills.

4. Put the tray in the refrigerator.

5. When the Jell-O is set (after about 4 hours), carefully remove it from the containers by coaxing it out with the tip of a warm knife. Or run tap water on the outside of the containers.

6. Invert the lenses onto clear plastic wrap or glass and place them over a sheet of newspaper.

WHAT'S GOING ON?

If light is bent before it gets to your eyes, it can change the picture that forms in your eyes. The Jell-O lenses bend light to make the picture in your eyes bigger. This makes the images on the newspaper look bigger than they actually are.

WHAT ELSE YOU CAN DO

Try all the lenses on the same words, then look at different things with the lenses. Which lenses make the words look bigger? Which make them look wiggly?

GLENBOW MUSEUM

WHO WE ARE
We are a public museum that takes visitors on a lively journey into the heritage of the Canadian West, and on an exciting worldwide voyage, exploring other cultures.

Glenbow Museum
130 - 9th Avenue. S.E.
Calgary, Alberta   T2G 0P3

Tel: (403) 268-4100
School program bookings:
Tel: (403) 268-4110
Fax: (403) 262-4045
World Wide Web: www.glenbow.org

Days and Hours
Mid May to mid September, open daily, 9:00 a.m. to 5:00 p.m.; mid September to mid May, open Tuesday to Sunday, closed Monday.

Admission Fees
Adults - $7.00; Students, Seniors - $5.00; Children under 6 free; Family - $25.00.

WHAT WE DO
We provide the public with an opportunity to view our extensive collections. The multidisciplinary aspect of our collections and services are reflected in changing exhibitions, lectures, films, tours, and other public programming.

Programs Offered
All ages. **Tours:** School tours of native galleries, western Canadian history galleries, art and mineralogy. Call to book. Customized tours available on request. **Workshops and Special Programs:** Throughout the year, we offer many activities and programs: including tours, lectures, workshops and special events. **Outreach:** Museokits—miniature museums in a portable suitcase, with objects for display and study, educator notes with student-centred activities, and support materials. Two weeks - $25.00. Call to book.

Resources
Books, speakers, presentations, slide shows, videos, films, magazines, portable exhibits, museokits.

Facilities
Auditorium, museum, classroom, library, bookstore/gift shop, cafeteria, snack bar.

DYEING WITH PLANT MATERIALS

Note: Adult supervision is required for this activity.

WHAT YOU NEED
- Heat source
- Stainless steel pan
- Strainer
- Long-handled spoon or stick
- Potassium aluminum sulphate
- Pure wool yarn (white)
- Several types of plant materials (e.g., red and brown onion skins, red cabbage, beetroot, spinach, red, green or brown leaves)

WHAT TO DO
1. Fill a medium pan two-thirds with water and add a handful of plant material.
2. Simmer the material, just under a boil, until the water becomes tinted.
3. Strain out all plant material.
4. Add 2.5 mL of the potassium aluminum sulphate.
5. Wrap the desired amount of wool around fingers, then use the long end to make a simple knot around the loop to prevent tangling.
6. Carefully place the wool in the hot water.
7. Leave it in the water until it has absorbed the dye.
8. Take the wool out and let it dry. You can use the wool for lots of projects.

WHAT'S GOING ON?
The natural pigments found in plant materials are released in the boiling water, and are absorbed by the wool. The potassium aluminum sulphate is a mordant, which is a chemical that fixes a dye by combining with the dye to form an insoluble compound. An insoluble compound won't dissolve in water.

WHAT ELSE YOU CAN DO
Try using only one type of plant material at a time. What happens? Can you predict what colour the dye will be?

GRAIN ACADEMY

WHO WE ARE
We are a non-profit organization operated by the Alberta Wheat Pool, a cooperative owned by Alberta farmers.

Grain Academy
Roundup Centre
Box 1060
Stampede Park
Calgary, Alberta T2P 2K8
Tel: (403) 263-4594

Days and Hours
Monday to Friday, 10:00 a.m. to 4:00 p.m.

Admission Fees
Donation.

WHAT WE DO
We provide tours of our facility and explain how grains are grown, handled, processed, and transported for world use.

Programs Offered
Preschool, elementary, junior and senior high school, adult, senior citizen.
Tours: Tour is one and a half hours long and includes a film on pioneering, a working model of a grain elevator, a large train model showing the rail track through the Rocky Mountains and how grain is handled and loaded onto ships.

Resources
Teacher kits, presentations, information sheets.

Facilities
Museum, exhibits, interpretive centre.

SEEDY SOCKS

WHAT YOU NEED

- Magnifying glass
- White paper
- Woollen socks
- Packets of seeds (optional)

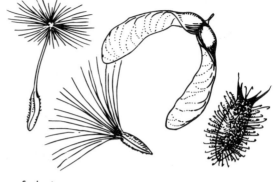

WHAT TO DO

1. Visit a garden, a school yard, or any place where there may be different types of plants.

2. If it is okay with your parents, put on an old pair of fuzzy socks over your shoes and walk around in a grassy or bushy area. (Go with a friend or family member.)

3. Remove your socks and notice the various seeds clinging to them. Pick the seeds off and examine them under a magnifying glass.

4. Place the seeds on a piece of white paper for easier viewing. How are the seeds different? How are they the same?

5. See if you can find which plants the seeds came from.

WHAT'S GOING ON?

Seed "dispersal" is when seeds are scattered over wide areas. This is a plant's survival technique. It prevents overcrowding near parent plants. Some seeds catapult into the air through "expulsion". People help seeds get around because some seeds are in burrs with little hooks that cling to clothing.

WHAT ELSE YOU CAN DO

Put the seeds in a small bag and keep them in the refrigerator for one week. Then plant the seeds in a pot of soil and see what sprouts. Keeping the seeds in the refrigerator is like having them go through a cold winter, which they usually do before sprouting.

GRASSROOTS N.W. - ENVIRONMENTAL AWARENESS SOCIETY

WHO WE ARE
We are a volunteer association that focuses on educating and encouraging positive individual and community environmental action.

Grassroots N.W. - Environmental Awareness Society
343 Scenic Acres Dr. N.W.
Calgary, Alberta   T3L 1T6

Tel: (403) 239-8231
Fax: (403) 239-8231 (call first)

WHAT WE DO
We conduct field trips, adult education programs and other programs dealing with the environment: recycling, waste minimization, xeriscaping, etc.

Programs Offered
Elementary, adult, community, teacher training. **Tours:** Field trips on the natural and cultural history of Nose Hill Natural Environmental Park available for teachers or youth leaders. **Workshops and Special Programs:** Adult education programs on such topics as recycling, waste minimizing and xeriscaping. We operate at the outdoor farmer's market at Northland Village Mall on Tuesdays all summer from 4:00 to 8:00 p.m. **Outreach:** Slide show for groups on Nose Hill Park and endangered fescue grassland. Readings by author and illustrator Nancy Hansen of books entitled: *Going on a Garbage Hunt* and *Let's Compost* (appropriate for ECS to Grade 3).

Resources
Books, including *Exploring Nose Hill: a Hands-on Field Guide*, teacher kits, speakers, presentations, and slide shows.

Facilities
Field trips to Nose Hill Park.

ORGANIC—WHAT'S THE DIFFERENCE?

WHAT YOU NEED

- small pieces of food—one from the normal area of your local grocery store and one from the organic section of the store, or from a specialty store that carries organic produce. Food that you are likely to find as both organic and non-organic include apples, carrots, beets, or broccoli.

WHAT TO DO

1. Wash and prepare both of the items as you would normally, keeping track of which item is which.

2. Examine both, noting which item appears more appetizing.

3. Ask a friend to do a "taste test", or do it yourself. Taste both items to see which one tastes better.

WHAT'S GOING ON?

You may or may not notice any difference, but usually organic produce is blemished or is less visually appealing than produce that has been grown with pesticides and herbicides. Organic produce is often more flavourful. In any case, you can be assured that the organic item was grown in a manner that minimizes environmental risks.

What is organic food? According to Alberta Agriculture and the organic producers of Alberta, "organic farming is a production process that avoids the use of chemical fertilizers, herbicides, pesticides or growth regulators. The primary focus of organic production is to maintain soil health and develop environmentally sustainable farm ecosystems".

Organic foods that are grown or raised in Alberta include vegetables, grain and livestock. These products can be purchased in Calgary at some of the regular grocers, at many specialty health food stores and at the many farmers' markets.

HEART AND STROKE FOUNDATION OF ALBERTA AND N.W.T.

WHO WE ARE

We are the only voluntary health agency in Canada devoted entirely to fighting heart disease and stroke.

Heart and Stroke Foundation of Alberta and N.W.T.
1825 Park Road S.E.
Calgary, Alberta   T2G 3Y6

Tel: (403) 264-5549
Fax: (403) 237-0803
E-mail: ramageb@hsfacal.org

WHAT WE DO

The mission of the Heart and Stroke Foundation of Alberta and N.W.T. is to further the study, prevention and reduction of disability and death from heart disease and stroke through research, public information and promotion of healthy lifestyles. We conduct campaigns, special events, the *Jump Rope for Heart* fund-raising program, memoriums and bequests.

Resources

We have a wealth of information about heart and brain health, available to the public. Books, newsletter, teacher kits, speakers, presentations, slide shows/videos/films, magazines, information sheets.

HEARTFELT

WHAT YOU NEED
- Sheet of stiff paper or small cardboard tube
- Watch that indicates seconds

WHAT TO DO

1. Roll the sheet of paper into a tube and put it against a friend's chest. Listen to their heart beating. Can you hear two sounds during every heartbeat: lub-DUB . . . lub-DUB . . . lub-DUB?

2. Using three fingers, gently push down on the artery beneath the skin of your left wrist. Can you feel your pulse?

3. With your fingers still on your wrist, count the number of times your pulse beats in 15 seconds.

4. Multiply this number by 4 to find your resting pulse per minute.

5. Try it twice to see if you get the same result.

WHAT'S GOING ON?
You can tell how fast your heart pumps by counting your pulse beats. Healthy, fit hearts can do the same amount of pumping work with fewer beats than a weak heart. The rhythmic contraction of the heart is the "heartbeat". Although you think you hear a heartbeat, you are actually hearing the heart valves opening and slapping shut. When the heart pumps, it forces blood out into the arteries. Each time the heart beats, the artery walls expand and contract once to produce one "pulse beat".

WHAT ELSE YOU CAN DO
Take your pulse while sitting, standing, and lying down. Hop 25 times and take your pulse. Hop 100 times and take your pulse. Can you change your pulse rate by imagining a time when you felt excitement or fear?

HERITAGE PARK HISTORICAL VILLAGE

WHO WE ARE
We are a historical village and museum. Visitors can see how science and technology related to life in days gone by.

Heritage Park Historical Village
1900 Heritage Drive S.W.
Calgary, Alberta   T2V 2X3

Tel: (403) 259-1900
Fax: (403) 252-3528
Information line: (403) 259-1910

Admission Fees and Hours
Please call the information line for details.

WHAT WE DO
We conduct programs for school groups and offer an exciting range of program opportunities when fully open in May, June, July and August.

Programs Offered
Preschool, elementary, junior and senior high school, youth groups, adult, family, community, senior citizen, teacher training. **Tours:** Self-guided science enthusiasts can explore the science behind heritage gardens, steam powered engines, a nature hike with interpretive signs and more. **Workshops and Special Programs:** Special events in the summer focus on the railway and steam power, and traditional agricultural techniques. **Outreach:** Call for further information.

Resources
Newsletter, memberships, speakers, information sheets.

Facilities
Museum, exhibits, classroom/science room, interpretive centre, live animals, library, bookstore/giftshop, cafeteria/snack bar, amusement rides, nature trail.

MAKING OLD-FASHIONED PAINT FROM MILK

WHAT YOU NEED

- Water

- Non-fat, dry milk powder

- Colouring materials, like coloured chalk ground into powder, berry juice (strawberry or cherry), beet juice, or coloured earth

WHAT TO DO

1. Mix the powdered milk and water in a large container. Use a 1:1 proportion (e.g., 250 mL water to 250 mL milk powder). You should get a thick, paint-like liquid. If the liquid is too thick, add more water. If it is too thin, add more milk powder.

2. Add the colouring material to the liquid. Add more for an intense colour, less for a paler shade.

3. Use your milk paint to paint a picture.

WHAT'S GOING ON?

Paint is used to colour and protect objects from weather and use. In the old days, farmers did not have access to the same kind of paint we use today. To protect their barns, homes and furniture, they used paint made from things easily found around their farms, namely milk, berry juices, and coloured earth.

HOPE PROGRAM

WHO WE ARE
We are an organ and tissue procurement agency for Southern Alberta.

HOPE Program
Foothills Hospital, 1403 - 29 Street N.W.
Calgary, Alberta   T2N 2T9

Tel: (403) 283-2243
Fax: (403) 270-3783

WHAT WE DO
We teach classes on donor awareness and transplantation.

Programs Offered
High school, post-secondary credit, teacher training, adult, family, community, handicapped, senior citizen, youth groups.

Resources
Slide shows, videos, films, information sheets, portable exhibits.

KEEP THEM GOING

WHAT YOU NEED

- Used toys with one or more worn out parts (bulbs, batteries, wheels, etc.)
- Repair material (this may be salvaged from other toys, improvised or purchased)

WHAT TO DO

1. Find a toy that has been a favourite but is now broken. If you really like it, you have probably kept it even though you can no longer play with it.

2. Ask yourself if there is any way it could be repaired. If it's a battery-operated toy, perhaps it just needs a new battery. If it's a flashlight, it might just need a new bulb. A car might only need a new circular object to replace a tire. A stuffed animal might just need new button eyes and a fresh outfit.

3. Keep in mind that not all toys can be repaired. If this is the case for the toy you are looking at, see if there are any parts that can be used to fix another toy. If so, it can be used in a positive way rather than just thrown out.

4. As you look for toys to repair, keep these things in mind:
   - You're fixing something that was loved before and can still be loved.
   - You're prolonging the life of the toy, so it can give more enjoyment.
   - You're making sure that working parts are not wasted.

WHAT'S GOING ON?

In this activity, you are keeping the life of a toy going by finding replacement parts for it. This is like organ donation, where people give some of their "parts" to help other people live longer. Ask an adult to explain organ donation to you.

WHAT ELSE YOU CAN DO

Ask an adult to show you the back of their driver's licence, where they sign up to be an organ donor in case of an accident.

INGLEWOOD BIRD SANCTUARY

WHO WE ARE
We are a wildlife refuge area in the middle of Calgary. We have 80 acres, featuring 2.5 km of walking trails through riverine forest, along the Bow River and beside a lagoon. Over 270 bird species and 300 plant species have been observed. We are a protected site—no feeding wildlife, no dogs, bicycles or in-line skates allowed.

Inglewood Bird Sanctuary
2425 - 9th Avenue S.E.
Calgary, Alberta

Tel: (403) 269-8289 (Program information and booking)
　　 (403) 269-6688 (Sanctuary and wildlife information)
Fax: (403) 221-3775

Admission Fees
By donation.

Days and Hours
Visitor Centre: April 1 to September 30: Monday to Thursday 9:00 a.m. to 8:00 p.m. Friday to Sunday and holidays 9:00 a.m. to 5:00 p.m.; October 1 to March 31: 10:00 a.m. to 4:00 p.m. (closed Mondays, November 11, December 25 and 26).

WHAT WE DO
We provide nature-related courses and programs run by City of Calgary naturalist staff, who are based at the sanctuary. We answer enquiries about wildlife and provide summer daycamp programs.

Programs Offered
All ages. **Tours:** Naturalists lead nature tours (fee involved) or groups can go on self-guided tours. Pre-registration required. Self-guided "Adventure Packs" also available for rent to groups. **Workshops and Special Programs:** Custom presentations on nature-related topics can be provided. Courses for families and adults offered. On-site nature programs available designed for pre-school to high school. **Outreach:** Curriculum-fit programs available off-site and at the sanctuary include wetlands, flight, owls, bird adaptations, and other natural history topics. **Summer Camps:** 5-day nature and discovery daycamps for ages 6 to 9; children visit a variety of habitats to explore the world of birds, insects, mammals and plants.

Facilities
Exhibits, classroom, interpretive centre.

FRESH AIR ADVENTURE

WHAT YOU NEED
- Hardcovered notebook
- Pen or pencil
- Camera (optional)

WHAT TO DO

1. Before beginning your nature exploration, start a family nature notebook. In this book, you can record trips taken, observations made, pictures, etc.

2. The list below consists of several ideas for walks:

- **Mini walk** — look for things smaller than a loonie.

- **Colour walk** — search for natural objects in a variety of colours (pink, orange, blue, black, green, purple, yellow, brown, rust, grey, etc.).

- **Senses walk** — use your eyes, ears and nose to see, hear and smell a variety of different things. Make a list to see who can identify the most things using each of the senses (touch and taste not recommended).

- **What's new walk** — keep track of each new discovery while on the trail.

- **In search of. . . walk** — scavenger hunt theme. Make a list of things to find as you walk.

- **Shutterbug walk** — take a disposable camera with you, to take pictures of the adventure.

- **Make up your own unique family walks!**

BE CAREFUL!
Agree on what to do if someone gets lost (blow a whistle, meet somewhere).

JUNIOR FOREST WARDENS

WHO WE ARE
We are a program sponsored by Alberta Land and Forest Services, part of the Alberta government department, Alberta Environmental Protection.

Junior Forest Wardens
8660 Bearspaw Dam Road N.W.
P.O. Box 70028, Bowness Postal Station
Calgary, Alberta   T3B 5K3

Tel: (403) 297-8850/51
Fax: (403) 297-8865

Membership Fees
Varies—please call for information.

WHAT WE DO
We offer instruction for youngsters from 6 to 18 years old in forestry, woodstravel (outdoor living skills), ecology (wildlife), and leadership, through family-oriented club programs.

Programs Offered
Programs and Special Events: National Forestry week (first week of May), ongoing tree planting, district campouts, provincial campouts, national campouts, leader training, outdoor living skills, primitive skills. We also have a summer employment program—*Junior Forest Rangers* for 16- to 18-year-olds interested in forestry or a forestry-related career.

Resources
Books, newsletter, teacher kits, memberships, presentations, slide shows/ videos/ films, portable exhibits, equipment.

Note: To set up a Junior Forest Warden Club in your area or neighborhood, you need a minimum of four adults and six children. Please call to arrange a meeting with Rick Wolcott, Southern Regional Supervisor, Forestry Youth Programs.

FINDING YOUR TREE

WHAT YOU NEED
- Blindfold
- Partner
- An area with lots of trees

WHAT TO DO
1. Find a spot with trees.
2. Have one person put the blindfold on.
3. The person without the blindfold leads the other person in a path around the trees.
4. Bring the blindfolded person to a tree.
5. Let them feel the tree with their hands.
6. Walk them around the trees again.
7. Remove the blindfold.
8. Ask the person to find their tree.
9. Now switch.

WHAT'S GOING ON?
You use your sense of touch to explore the tree and find out its characteristics. You then have to translate that information from "touch" to "sight" to find your tree after the blindfold has been removed.

WHAT ELSE YOU CAN DO
Try to identify the type of tree you are touching while you are blindfolded.

JUST IMAGINE ENVIRONMENTAL SOCIETY OF ALBERTA

WHO WE ARE

We are a non-profit society that educates people in the importance of reducing, reusing and recycling.

Just Imagine Environmental Society of Alberta
Brentwood Village Mall
530, 3630 Brentwood Road N.W.
Calgary, Alberta   T2L 1K8

Tel: (403) 289-1016

Days and Hours

Thursday, Friday and Saturday: noon to 5:00 p.m.

WHAT WE DO

We sell industrial discards in our Just Imagine store and teach people to create useful items out of the discards so they don't end up in landfills. Children, artists and teachers recycle these discards into science and enviro-art projects.

Programs Offered

Preschool, elementary, junior and senior high school, post-secondary, youth groups, adult, family, community, handicapped, senior citizen, teacher training. **Workshops and Special Programs:** We strive to educate children and adults in the importance of reusing recycled materials to extend their life and prevent them from ending up in landfills. We also have a new and unique environmental education touring program. Through a colourful slide presentation, we look at what happens to our garbage after it gets picked up, where it goes and what it becomes. This program is geared to Grades 3 and up for the *Waste In Our World* science unit. Book ahead (small fee).

Resources

Speakers, presentations, slide shows, information sheets.

Facilities

Store/workshop area.

WEATHER WATCH WIND CHIMES

WHAT YOU NEED
- Discarded aluminum items such as used pie plates, TV dinner trays, etc.
- Cardboard
- String, wire or dental floss
- Paint, markers, stickers or glitter
- Single hole punch
- Tape, scissors, paper clips

WHAT TO DO
1. Decide on a shape for your wind chime pieces and, using scissors, carefully cut the aluminum into those shapes.
2. Cut a rectangular shape from the cardboard. This will be the hanger.
3. Decorate the aluminum pieces. Keep them shiny to reflect the sun.
4. Make a small hole in each with a hole punch. Tie the string, wire or dental floss onto the hole and knot to secure. Attach the other end of the string, wire or dental floss to the cardboard hanger.
5. Punch a hole at each end of the hanger. Tie each end of a piece of string onto the holes to create a hanger hoop.
6. Hang outside in a location where it will be free to blow in the wind.
7. Keep track of how much your wind chime is blowing, and what direction the wind is coming from. When your wind chime is still, what type of weather is it? When it's blowing a lot, what is the weather? Does the weather depend on the wind direction? By keeping track over several weeks, you might see patterns that allow you to predict what the weather may be like.

WHAT'S GOING ON?
Scientists who study weather are called meteorologists. They measure wind speed with an instrument called an anemometer. Your wind chime behaves in the wind in a similar way. It can indicate how hard the wind is blowing (wind speed) and what direction the wind is coming from. This information, along with temperature, air pressure, humidity and cloud cover, is used to help scientists predict what the weather will be like. They look for patterns.

BE CAREFUL!
The edges of cut aluminum can be very sharp so handle carefully!

KANANASKIS FOREST EDUCATION PARTNERSHIP

WHO WE ARE
We are an education program developed by the University of Calgary - Kananaskis Field Stations, Alberta Environmental Protection - Land and Forest Service, and FEESA, an environmental education society.

Kananaskis Forest Education Partnership
c/o Kananaskis Field Stations
University of Calgary
Biosciences 186,
Calgary, Alberta   T2N 1N4

Tel: (403) 220-5355
Fax: (403) 673-3671
E-mail: mmappin@acs.ucalgary.ca

Meeting Place
Jumping Pound Demonstration Forest and Barrier Lake Forestry Trails.

WHAT WE DO
The partnership offers forestry education programs to increase public understanding of the ecology and sustainable management of Alberta's forest ecosystems. Curriculum-based field studies are provided at the Jumping Pound Demonstration Forest and Barrier Lake Forestry Trails; both within an hour's drive from Calgary, in Kananaskis Country.

Programs Offered
Elementary, junior and senior high school, youth groups, community, teacher training.

Resources
Teacher kits, information sheets, equipment, lesson plans for Jumping Pound Demonstration Forest.

Facilities
Exhibits, classroom, interpretative centre, interpretative trails.

EVERY TREE TELLS A STORY

WHAT YOU NEED
• Trees!

WHAT TO DO

1. Every living thing is different and trees are no exception. Each tree grows under unique environmental conditions that dictate how it looks. By knowing what to look for, you can actually "read" a tree's life history.

2. Find an interesting tree on a walk through the woods, in the park or in your own backyard. Make notes and draw sketches as you go. What to look for:

   Trunk is twisted — the tree might have had to avoid obstacles as it grew, such as a fence, rocks or other trees. Trees that grow on a slope twist so their heads can reach for the sun while their roots dig into the soil.

   Tree has an extra trunk — one or more extra trunks probably mean that the original trunk was damaged in some way when the tree was young. It might have been broken off by a deer or nibbled off by a hungry beaver.

   Scars on the tree's bark — you can still see where branches were that are long gone. Old injuries can be seen where the bark grows in a circular or irregular pattern. These could be caused by animals eating the bark, by lightning or fire, by insects or disease, or by people.

   Tall, narrow shape — the tree probably grew away from other objects, perhaps on its own out in a meadow.

   Condition of the leaves — the leaves will tell you how the tree is "feeling" right now. If the leaves are drooping or curling under, it is not feeling too well. It may be undernourished, thirsty, or sick.

   What is the tree's "neighbourhood" like? — Are other plants crowding it (competition)? Is there a nearby source of moisture? Lots of sunlight or only a little? All of these factors can greatly affect your tree's growth.

WHAT'S GOING ON?
Foresters are responsible for the management of the forests in Alberta. They look for the same kind of information that you collected, and use it to decide on how best to protect this precious natural resource.

WHAT ELSE YOU CAN DO
Make a tree bark rubbing using paper and pencil. Count the number of rings on a cut tree trunk. The number of rings tells the tree's age.

THE LEIGHTON CENTRE

WHO WE ARE
We are a non-profit organization dedicated to the goal of bringing art and nature together in our unique setting.

The Leighton Centre
Site 31, Box 9, RR 8
Calgary, Alberta   T2J 2T9

Tel: (403) 931-3636
Fax: (403) 931-3597

Admission Fees
$8.00 per child, minimum $130.00 per studio.

Days and Hours
9:30 a.m. to 3:00 p.m.

WHAT WE DO
We offer a unique setting for exploring creativity through hands-on experiences using various art and craft media.

Programs Offered
Elementary, junior high school. **Tours:** Daily field trips available Monday to Friday from 9:30 a.m. to 3:00 p.m. We can accommodate three classes a day. A day includes two crafts, nature hike, gallery and museum tour, and classroom banner. **Workshops and Special Programs:** Brownie and Guide badge programs - Saturdays only. **Summer Camps:** Offered weekly throughout the summer. Transportation from Calgary provided. Ages 6 to 12. Arts, crafts, nature hikes, games, songs and a variety show.

Resources
Information sheets.

Facilities
Museum, three art studios and art gallery.

MAKING A SIMPLE PLANT PRESS

WHAT YOU NEED

- 2 pieces of thick, corrugated cardboard 23 cm x 30 cm (heavy packing boxes are good sources of thick cardboard)

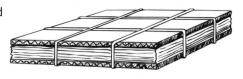

- 6 to 10 sheets of newspaper, folded in half, or cut to the same size as the cardboard

- 4 heavy-duty rubber bands

- Heavy object(s) to weigh the press down (bricks or heavy books)

WHAT TO DO

1. Collect a plant specimen from your yard or school grounds. Try to collect only common or "weedy" types of plants. Do not collect rare or endangered plants, such as wild orchids. Be careful not to disturb or injure other plants when you are collecting your specimen.

2. Create a "sandwich" with the newspaper sheets between the cardboard pieces.

3. Carefully place the plant specimen between the newspaper sheets, making sure that there are several sheets on top and underneath the plant. Also make sure that the plant is spread out and its leaves are flat.

4. Tightly secure the plant press with the rubber bands.

5. Place the bricks or heavy books on the plant press.

6. Wait a few days until your plant specimen has dried. Remove it carefully from the press and tape it to a piece of heavy paper, or a page in a scrapbook.

WHAT ELSE YOU CAN DO

Collect different kinds of plants at different times of the year. When you tape them to your scrapbook pages, record where and when you found them. Look at pictures of plants in books from the library and see if you can identify the plants. Write the names of the plants in your scrapbook.

MEDICAL EXAMINER'S OFFICE

WHO WE ARE

We are the Chief Medical Examiner's Office operating within the Alberta Department of Justice under the Fatality Inquiries Act.

Medical Examiner's Office
4070 Bowness Road N.W.
Calgary, Alberta   T3B 3R7

Tel: (403) 297-8123
Fax: (403) 297-3429
E-mail: vanhaeftens@just.gov.ab.ca

Admission Fees

Maintenance fee, $1.00/person.

Days/Hours

Tuesday and Thursday, 1:30 p.m. to 3:00 p.m.

Size of Groups

Maximum 32.

WHAT WE DO

We investigate instances of sudden, unexplained or unnatural death. This represents about one third of all deaths in Alberta.

Programs Offered

Grades 8, 9, high school, teacher training, youth groups. Tours: The *Death-in-the-Gym* program was developed with a grant from Science Alberta Foundation. It is based on forensic science and is a video and interactive computer investigation of a fictitious death scene. Attendees should be an interested and relevant group. The program is largely self-administered.

Facilities

Museum, exhibits and displays.

COLD FACTS

WHAT YOU NEED

- 2 baking potatoes (as close in size as possible)
- Cooking thermometer (measuring up to 230°C/450°F)
- Watch with a second hand
- Oven (microwave or conventional)
- Paper and pencil

WHAT TO DO

1. Place one of the potatoes in the oven and bake at 200°C/375°F for one hour.

2. When done, put it on a plate and insert the cooking thermometer right into the centre. Record the highest temperature reached (after about two minutes). This is the temperature at "time 0".

3. Leave the thermometer in the potato and each minute thereafter, record the temperature and the elapsed time. Continue until the temperature no longer changes. You now have a cooling scale to use later.

4. Have an adult cook the other potato for the same amount of time at the same temperature. Ask them to write down the exact time they took it out of the oven. After a while, go and check the temperature of the potato.

5. Record the temperature using the method in Step 3, and compare it with the cooling scale you made earlier. Can you work out how long it's been since the potato was removed from the oven?

WHAT'S GOING ON?

Any object cools quickly at first, but as its temperature gets closer to that of the surrounding air, the cooling rate slows. When it reaches the same temperature as the air, it maintains that temperature. Objects of similar size and material have predictable cooling rates. So, if you make a scale, you can use it to find out how long something has been cooling. Medical Examiners and forensic scientists use cooling scales. When a person dies, their body temperature immediately begins to cool. By taking the temperature of a body and comparing it to a scale for similar-sized individuals, Medical Examiners try to determine the time of death, which can be an important clue.

BE CAREFUL!

Have an adult take the potato out of the oven. It could burn you.

MINK HOLLOW FARM

WHO WE ARE
We are a small farm involved in raising waterfowl and rabbits.

Mink Hollow Farm
R.R. 2
Cochrane, Alberta   T0L 0W0

Tel: (403) 932-6322
E-mail: becker@cpsc.ucalgary.ca

WHAT WE DO
We sell duck-hatching kits (ducks and geese only) for schools and pre-schools. We also rent out rabbits for classrooms and other groups.

Programs Offered
Preschool, elementary, junior and senior high school, family, youth groups. No tours are available.

Resources
Teacher kits, information sheets, duck-hatching kits. Hatching kits include about 150 pages of printed material, references and activities.

CREATING A BIRD HABITAT

WHAT YOU NEED

- An old lid or tray
- Some stones
- Water
- Plastic pop bottle with top
- String
- 2 sticks
- Peanuts

WHAT TO DO

1. Build a bird bath from the lid or tray. Make sure the inside is rough, not slippery. Put a few stones in it and make sure to change the water every day.

2. Make two holes near the bottom of the plastic pop bottle. Thread the string through the holes so you can hang the bottle upside down.

3. Draw a line about halfway down the bottle and make ten slits in the bottle from the line to the top.

4. Push the sticks through slots in the bottle to make a perch for the birds.

5. Pour the peanuts into the bottle and hang it upside down.

WHAT'S GOING ON?

Birds often need help to survive through the winter. You can help by building a bird habitat. Birds need food, and water for drinking and bathing. Make a bird habitat and you will be able to see all kinds of birds in your yard.

WHAT ELSE YOU CAN DO

You can build a little "wild area" in your yard. Just put some logs and flat stones around a small area of your yard. Don't plant grass or flowers there, just let it grow wild. It will make a good home for bugs and insects. These will provide good food for birds.

MOUNT ROYAL COLLEGE, COLLEGE KIDS' CAMPS

WHO WE ARE
We are action-packed, summer day camps for children that allow them to discover, create, explore and experiment!

Mount Royal College
Credit-Free Registration Office
4825 Richard Road S.W.
Calgary, Alberta   T3E 6K6

Tel: (403) 240-8943
Information
Tel: (403) 240-6001
Fax: (403) 240-7244
World Wide Web: http://www.mtroyal.ab.ca

Days and Hours
Monday through Friday, 8:30 a.m. to 4:30 p.m. Free before-and-after care available from 7:30 a.m. to 8:30 a.m. and 4:30 p.m. to 6:00 p.m., July and August.

WHAT WE DO
We offer special summer events for children that include the following science-related subjects: geology/paleontology, psychology, aviation, computer science, criminology, science and computers.

Programs Offered
Elementary, junior high school.

IT'S . . . ALIVE!

WHAT YOU NEED
- 2 carrots (preferably fresh, with green leaves still attached)
- 2 vegetable storage Ziplock bags (with breathing holes), or poke small holes into a regular Ziplock bag using a toothpick
- Small knife

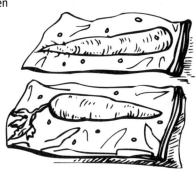

WHAT TO DO
1. Find two carrots similar in size and shape, and preferably picked at the same time to ensure a "fair test".

2. Cut the green leafy top off one of them.

3. Place the "leafless" and leafy carrot in separate bags. Carefully seal them.

4. Leave both bags together in a corner of your refrigerator for about one week.

5. After one week, take both carrots out of the fridge and closely examine them. How does their appearance differ? Is one softer than the other? Now taste them. Which one tastes fresher?

WHAT'S GOING ON?
Did you ever wonder if you kill a plant by picking it? This experiment shows you the answer. Plants consist of roots and green leaves (some also have woody material). The roots provide a path for nutrients and water, and the green leaves use the sun and air to produce their own food through a process called photosynthesis. As long as the roots and leaves are doing their job, a plant will survive. When you pick a carrot, you pick both the green leaves and the root (the part that we eat). This means that the plant still has what it needs to survive. If you replanted it in a nice, sunny spot, it would be just fine. However, by putting the leaves in the fridge where it is dark, the leaves become useless because they need light to do their job. The carrot with the leaves attached tries to survive by giving up some of the nutrients and water from the root to nourish the leaves. This makes the root soft and dried out. The carrot root with no leaves did not need to do this, so the nutrients stayed in the carrot where it could be more enjoyed by us.

WHAT ELSE YOU CAN DO
Cut off the green leaves and about 1 cm of the carrot top. Put in a dish of water in a sunny place. See how well the plant survives. Try radishes or beets too.

BE CAREFUL!
Let an adult help you cut the top off the carrot.

OPERATION MINERVA

WHO WE ARE
We are an organization of female science and technology professionals dedicated to encouraging female students to follow a career in science or technology.

Operation Minerva
2728 Crawford Road N.W.
Calgary, Alberta T2L 1E1

Tel: (403) 282-6431
Fax: (403) 284-4750

Admission Fees
$15.00/person.

Size of Groups
Maximum 120 (Calgary); 35 - 50 (Peace River, Medicine Hat, Red Deer, Athabasca).

WHAT WE DO
We represent Operation Minerva across the province and organize a career conference annually to encourage young women (13 years, Grade 8) to choose careers in science and technology. Most conferences run for two days, one day job-shadowing a science and technology female professional, one day of science and technology workshops presented by female science and technology professionals.

Programs Offered
Junior high school. **Field Trips:** Job shadowing, one full day at resource companies, clinics, hospitals, etc. **Outreach:** In Calgary: available to two female students from Calgary Board of Education and Calgary Regional Catholic School Board junior high schools. Outreach program availability varies in other locations. **Workshops and Special Programs:** Criminology, electronics, bicycle mechanics, microbiology, engineering, computers, biomechanics.

Resources
Handbook with information on running a conference ($10.00).

EGG-CITING SCIENCE

WHAT YOU NEED

- 4 raw chicken eggs of equal size

- 1 egg carton

- Hardcover books of equal size and weight to make a 60-cm stack (choose books with a surface that can be wiped easily, or wrap them in plastic)

WHAT TO DO

1. Put the four eggs with their pointed ends down in the second and fifth rows of the egg carton.

2. Carefully place one book on the eggs in the open egg carton.

3. Continue adding books one at a time, balancing the books as you go, to see how tall a tower you can make without the eggs cracking.

WHAT'S GOING ON

An egg's shape—two dome shapes pushed together—makes it resistant to forces pressing inward (compression). This is why a hen can sit on eggs without breaking them. However, dome shapes are weak to forces pressing outward (tension), so a chick can easily peck its way out when hatching.

THE PETROLEUM COMMUNICATION FOUNDATION

WHO WE ARE

The Petroleum Communication Foundation is a non-profit organization with the mandate to create an awareness and understanding for Canada's petroleum industry.

The Petroleum Communication Foundation
214, 311 - 6 Avenue S.W.
Calgary, Alberta   T2P 3H2

Tel: (403) 264-6064
Fax: (403) 237-6286
E-mail: pcomm@pcf.ab.ca
World Wide Web: http://www.pcf.ab.ca

WHAT WE DO

We provide information about Canada's petroleum industry to the public as well as industry professionals.

Resources

Resources available for elementary, junior and senior high schools, and post-secondary students. Web-page, speaker's bureau, slide and video collection, science curriculum materials, books, magazines, newspaper clippings, publications, portable exhibit, and natural gas and crude oil measurement poster.

Facilities

Library.

HEAVY OIL IN YOUR KITCHEN

WHAT YOU NEED

- Measuring cup or margarine container

- Mixing bowl

- 250 mL frozen peas or carrots

- 250 mL margarine

- Pan or sink partly filled with very warm water (not hot)

WHAT TO DO

1. If your margarine was purchased in squares, take the wrapping off the margarine and put the margarine into the measuring cup or used margarine container. If your margarine came from the store in a plastic container, leave it in there.

2. Lower the container into the pan or sink of warm water keeping water out of the container. Let the margarine soften and partially or totally melt. This margarine represents the heavy oil.

3. While the margarine is warming up, pour the frozen vegetables into the mixing bowl.

4. Stir them to make sure they are not all frozen together. Separate those that are in lumps. These vegetables represent the sand grains in the reservoir rock.

5. Once the margarine is melted, pour it over the vegetables, stirring gently to coat the vegetables thoroughly. The margarine should glue all or most of the vegetables together. You have now created a model of a rock with heavy oil in the pore spaces between the grains in the rock.

6. To extract your heavy oil from its reservoir rock, you will have to do the same thing that petroleum engineers do: warm up the rock, causing the oil to become more fluid (less viscous). Engineers sometimes use underground fires, but hot water (steam) is most commmonly used. For safety, we will use warm water.

7. Put your mixing bowl into the pan of warm water. Eventually, some of the margarine will be fluid enough to be poured out of the bowl and back into its original container. This is equivalent to the *recoverable oil*. Some margarine will always remain as a coating on the vegetables. The ratio of the recoverable oil to the total amount of oil that was in the reservoir rock (known as the *original oil in place*) gives you the *recovery factor*.

THE PETROLEUM SOCIETY

WHO WE ARE
We are an organization concerned with informing our members about petroleum-related information. We are also devoted to informing the public about career opportunities in the petroleum industry.

The Petroleum Society - Canadian Institute of Mining, Metallurgy and Petroleum
Suite 320, 101 - 6 Avenue S.W.
Calgary, Alberta   T2P 3P4

Tel: (403) 237-5112
Fax: (403) 262-4792
E-mail: petsoc@canpic.ca
World Wide Web: http://www.canpic.ca/petsoc

Meeting Place and Time
Special interest groups (monthly), annual technical meeting and petroleum show. Please call for further details.

Membership Fees
Student $15.00/year; Regular $100.00/year.

WHAT WE DO
Our main aim is to disseminate technical and non technical, petroleum-related information to our members through our monthly journal, meetings, annual technical meetings, monographs, and courses.

Programs Offered
High school, adults, youth groups.

Resources
Books, memberships, presentations, magazines (with membership).

Facilities
Exhibits/displays (annual technical meeting).

OIL AND WATER

WHAT YOU NEED

- 2 clear glasses or jars
- A few drops of vegetable oil
- A spoon
- Fake fur, fabric scraps, feathers, or stones (at least 2 of each)

WHAT TO DO

1. Fill both containers with equal amounts of water.
2. Add a few drops of oil to one container.
3. Stir the oil and water and let them sit for twenty minutes. What has happened to the oil?
4. Dip each of the objects into the water; one into the oily water and one into the other water.
5. Observe the objects after you have dipped them.

WHAT'S GOING ON?

Oil is less dense than water so it forms a layer on top of the water. Oil polluting our rivers, lakes and oceans does the same thing. It covers objects the same way your dipped objects were covered.

WHAT ELSE YOU CAN DO

1. Try cleaning up the objects with paper towels and water.
2. Try "booming the oil"—collecting the oil by skimming the surface using Popsicle sticks or a spoon.
3. Try cleaning the oil with cotton balls.
4. Add a few drops of detergent—what happens?

THINGS TO THINK ABOUT

What does oil do to our water and to the fish and other creatures that live in it? What happens to the birds that swim and dive in the water? What about wildlife and people who drink the water? Which clean-up methods would be safe? What can people do to keep the water clean in the first place?

RMEF - ROCKY MOUNTAIN ELK FOUNDATION

WHO WE ARE
We are an international, non-profit wildlife organization dedicated to the conservation of elk and other wildlife habitats in North America.

RMEF - Rocky Mountain Elk Foundation
P.O. Box 940
Rocky Mountain House, Alberta T0M 1T0

Calgary Chapter Address
140 Cedarpark Green S.W.
Calgary, Alberta T2W 2J9

Tel: (403) 251-1713
Fax: (403) 251-7672
E-mail: bishopbb@cadvision.com

Meeting Place and Time
November to May. Please call for details.

Membership Fees
$35.00 per year.

WHAT WE DO
RMEF is committed to supporting youth education on wildlife and their habitats.

Programs Offered
Elementary, junior high school. **Primary event:** Banquet and auction to raise funds for wildlife habitats. *WOW* magazine campaign.

Resources
Slide shows/videos/films, *WOW* magazine.

WHOSE FEET?

WHAT YOU NEED
- five fingers

WHAT TO DO
1. Take a look at the following pictures.

A P E	**CAT**	**PIG**	**H O R S E**
Plantigrade	Digitigrade	Even-toed ungulate	Odd-toed ungulate

2. Try holding your hands in the following positions and imagine how the different animals walk or run. Are there any differences? Can you think of any advantages one foot has over another?

Plantigrade	Digitigrade	Even-toed ungulate	Odd-toed ungulate

Put your hands flat on the table.	Put four fingers down but lift up the heel of your hand.	Put two middle fingers down and pull other fingers behind. Don't let them touch the table.	Squeeze all four fingers together with the tallest finger only on the table.

WHAT'S GOING ON?
How an animal stands on its feet is an adaptation to the way it lives. Think about how each animal lives and maybe you can figure out why its feet are the shape they are.

ROCKYVIEW WILDLIFE RECOVERY

WHO WE ARE

We are a wildlife rescue centre, that is also involved in teaching environmental education and wildlife research.

Rockyview Wildlife Recovery
Box 68
Madden, Alberta   TOM 1L0

Tel: (403) 946-2361
Fax: (403) 946-5689

Membership Fees

$28.00 per year or $48.00 for two years. Call for information on the volunteer program.

WHAT WE DO

We have field trips and special programs to teach people all about wildlife, nature, ecology and conservation.

Programs Offered

Elementary, junior and senior high school, youth groups, adults, families, community, handicapped, senior citizens. **Tours:** Field trips - maximum 25 people per group. Topics include anything to do with wildlife, nature, ecology, conservation. **Workshops and Special Programs:** Slide shows, hands-on demonstrations, crafts, workshops.

Resources

Newsletter, speakers, presentations, slide shows/videos/films, information sheets.

Facilities

Classroom, interpretive centre (in development), live animals.

FIND THE FOOD

WHAT YOU NEED

- 100 coloured toothpicks, pieces of wool, or pipe cleaners (about 25 of each of four colours). Be sure to include one colour that blends into the activity area, e.g., green for a green lawn.

WHAT TO DO

1. Scatter the coloured toothpicks, wool, or pipe cleaners over an area of about 200 square metres.

2. Ask your friends to play the roles of birds looking for bugs (the coloured objects) to eat. Each person will have a 'nest' where they will collect the coloured objects. The nest will be approximately 25 m from the feeding area.

3. One at a time, the birds (your friends) will run to the feeding area to find food. Each bird takes its turn and makes several flights. Only one bug can be caught per flight. Grab the first food you see.

4. After several flights, how many of each colour of bug has each person collected? What colour of food is the hardest to find? Why?

WHAT'S GOING ON?

Birds don't care what colour worms or insects they eat are, so they grab the first food they see. Birds can't run their hands over the ground, so they pick up bugs only after spotting them. You will notice that the coloured object that is most like the colour of the game area is the hardest food to find. Body colour is a form of adaptation that protects animals by allowing them to blend into their surroundings. This is called "camouflage". When an animal is camouflaged it is harder for its enemies to find. The female of most bird species is dull and drab, which serves as a protection while the bird is nesting. The male bird is often brightly coloured so that it stands out from its environment. In this way, it draws attention away from the nest.

ROYAL ASTRONOMICAL SOCIETY OF CANADA

WHO WE ARE
We are a non-profit, charitable organization devoted to advancing astronomy and related space sciences. The Wilson Coulee Observatory was opened in 1983 and has provided thousands of children an opportunity to view the night sky away from the city lights.

Royal Astronomical Society of Canada—Calgary Centre
c/o The Calgary Science Centre
P.O. Box 2100, Station M
Calgary Alberta   T2P 2M5

Tel: (403) 237-STAR
World Wide Web: http://www.syz.com/rasc/

Meeting Place and Time
Third Thursday of the month, 7:30 p.m., Calgary Science Centre, September through November and January through May.

Membership Fees
Adults $44.00/year; students $30.50/year. Membership includes observer's handbook, national and local newsletters.

Days and Hours
Tours of our observatory (located near Okotoks) by appointment only (small fee charged).

WHAT WE DO
We have an observing group, which meets at Wilson Coulee Observatory. Our active youth group for ages 10 to 18 meets at the Calgary Science Centre. We co-host the Alberta Star Party, near Caroline, usually in August or September.

Programs Offered
All ages. **Tours:** Children watch a slide presentation on astronomy and tour the society's large telescope, which they can look through (weather permitting). Call 237-STAR to book. **Outreach:** Volunteers visit schools to discuss astronomy and are available for teacher workshops describing hands-on projects for the classroom. (Book through the Science Hotline, Tel: 263-6226).

Resources
Books, newsletter, teacher kits, speakers.

Facilities
Classroom/science room, observatory.

USE THE STARS TO FIND YOUR WAY HOME

WHAT YOU NEED
- A clear, starry night

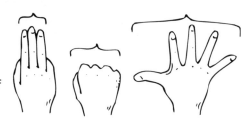

WHAT TO DO
1. Find the Big Dipper, part of the constellation Ursa Major, the great bear.

2. Find the two stars that form the edge of the Dipper's bowl on the side away from the handle. These are your "pointer stars".

3. Hold out your hand at arm's length. Notice the distance between the "pointer stars" is about the same as three finger widths. This distance is about 5°.

4. From the "pointer stars" to Polaris is 28°, or slightly more than five times the distance between the "pointer stars". Now, holding your hand at arm's length, put your thumb at the lip of the Dipper's bowl and your baby finger out along the line of the two "pointer stars". Your baby finger should appear to be close to Polaris, the North Star, which forms the end of the handle of the Little Dipper, Ursa Minor (the little bear).

5. Once you are looking at Polaris, the rest is easy: east is to your right, west is on your left, and south is behind you.

WHAT ELSE YOU CAN DO
Before your scurry home, you might want to take a short sky tour. In spring through early fall, following the curve of the Big Dipper's handle away from the bowl will lead you to orange Arcturus in the constellation Boötes, the herdsman. The top two stars in the bowl point at yellow Capella, in the charioteer, Auriga. Capella is best seen in late fall, winter and early spring. It is low along the northern horizon during the rest of the year.

SAE INTERNATIONAL

WHO WE ARE
We are the Society of Automotive Engineers, a member-driven organization of more than 69,000 professionals in 90 countries around the world.

SAE International
224 Hawkhill Court N.W.
Calgary, Alberta   T3G 2T8

Tel: (403) 239-7074
World Wide Web: http://www.sae.org/STUDENTS/awim.htm

Meeting Place and Time
Monthly meetings, usually at the Highlander Hotel, Calgary.

Membership Fees
$75.00 US/year, full members; $12.00 US/year students.

WHAT WE DO
We further the interest of all modes of self-propelled transportation by sea, land and air. Membership covers industry, government, education, consulting, etc.

Programs Offered
Elementary, junior high school. *A World in Motion* for elementary and secondary schools to explain principles of motion and transportation. Advanced projects supported in colleges and universities.

Resources
Newsletter, teacher kits, speakers, presentations.

MORE BOUNCE FOR YOUR BUCK

WHAT YOU NEED
- Various types of balls (tennis, ping-pong, golf, etc.)
- Metre stick
- Paper and pencil
- Piece of chalk
- Wall

WHAT TO DO
1. Place the metre stick upright, against a wall.
2. Mark the wall at the top of the metre stick.
3. Hold one of the balls at the mark on the wall. **Drop** (do not throw!) the ball and have a partner measure how high the ball bounces back up. Repeat this three times and record the results.
4. You can find the height of the average bounce by adding the three results together and dividing by 3. Record this number as well.
5. Repeat Steps 3 and 4 using the other balls.
6. What did you find out? What did the balls that bounced the highest have in common?

WHAT'S GOING ON?
By dropping the balls from the same height and recording the distance they rebounded, you are testing to see which type of material has the most stored energy. The more stored energy the ball has before you drop it, the higher it will bounce. Energy is the power to do work, and stored energy is just waiting to do work. Engineers look for ways to store energy to ensure it is there when needed. To play a particular game or sport, we need a ball with the right amount of bounce. A tennis ball that flies out of the court every time a racquet hits it, would not be a popular choice. Likewise, a golf ball that only went six or seven metres every time it was hit would be extremely frustrating. Engineers who design sports equipment test materials to find ones with just the right amount of bounce for the sport.

WHAT ELSE YOU CAN DO
Change the height from which you drop the balls to see if it changes the behaviour of the rebound. Try putting different kinds of material on the bounce surface (cloth, wood, water, etc.) and observe your results.

SAM LIVINGSTON FISH HATCHERY

WHO WE ARE
The Sam Livingston Fish Hatchery is part of the Provincial Fish Culture and Fisheries Management Program. The Fish Culture Program helps sustain or enhance recreational fishing opportunities in Alberta through fish stocking and public education.

Sam Livingston Fish Hatchery
1440 17A St. S.E.
Calgary, Alberta   T2G 4T9

Tel: (403) 297-6561
Tours: (403) 255-0970
Fax: (403) 297-2839

Days and Hours
Monday to Friday, 10:00 a.m. to 4:00 p.m., Saturday and Sunday 1:00 p.m. to 5:00 p.m.

Admission
Free.

WHAT WE DO
We give guided tours of various trout storage facilities, such as troughs and circular tanks, as well as tanks displaying different types of trout.

Tours Available
Tours are self-guided for individuals, or a volunteer might be available for groups of ten or more.

DINING OUT WITH TROUT

Note: Adult supervision is required for this activity.

WHAT YOU NEED

- Tin can of any size
- Cellophane
- 2 rubber bands
- Tape
- Plastic buckets
- Creek or small pond

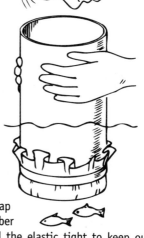

WHAT TO DO

1. To make a viewer, remove both ends of a tin can. Make sure there are no sharp edges by using tape to cover the edges. Stretch a piece of cellophane or other clear plastic wrap over one end and secure it with a thick rubber band. The plastic must be stretched flat and the elastic tight to keep out the water. You might want to stretch a second elastic 1 to 2 cm above the first one to secure the plastic even more so it does not flop around.

2. At the edge of the creek or small pond, place the plastic covered end of the can under the water surface and look through the bare end. This tool helps to get rid of the reflection of light from the water's surface so you will be able to see what goes on under the water.

3. Change the position of your viewer every two to three minutes to find out if location makes a difference to what you can see.

WHAT'S GOING ON?

Depending on the time of year, you should be able to see many aquatic or juvenile insects, fish and tadpoles.

WHAT ELSE YOU CAN DO

Bring ice-cream buckets and small plastic buckets and dip them into the water near the edges. Wait for the water to settle down and watch the insect life swimming around. Please put any creature you capture back in its home when you are finished looking.

BE CAREFUL!

Always remember to make sure that the place you are going to look is safe. Have your parents come with you to help out.

SCIENCE ALBERTA FOUNDATION

WHO WE ARE
We are a non-profit organization dedicated to promoting science literacy throughout Alberta. Our mission is to create and inspire innovative programs that will encourage Albertans to discover and share the excitement and relevance of science. We receive our core funding from the Alberta Lottery Fund, with additional funding from corporate donations. Our programs are made possible through the many partnerships formed with corporations, businesses, teachers, librarians, individuals, and communities.

Science Alberta Foundation
1200, 800 - 6th Avenue S.W.
Calgary, Alberta   T2P 3G3

Tel: (403) 260-1996
Fax: (403) 260-1165
E-mail: litebulb@saf.ab.ca
World Wide Web: www.freenet.calgary.ab.ca/saf/

WHAT WE DO
With a vision of creating centres for science in every Alberta community, we provide a variety of quality programs—hands-on science and technology workshops, summer institutes, travelling exhibitions, Science in a Crate, publications and special projects. Our exhibitions and activities are portable, flexible and accessible, for shipping throughout the province. We also support the Science Hotlines in Calgary, Edmonton, Medicine Hat and Peace River Country (Grande Prairie).

Programs Offered
Preschool, elementary, junior and senior high school, post-secondary, teacher and librarian training, parents, family, community, senior citizen, youth groups.

Resources (some fees apply)
Newsletter, travelling exhibitions, Science in a Crate, and publications: *Integrating Computers in the Classroom; Best of the Web; Let's Do Science; Science Begins at Home; Backyard Safari; Ready, Set Science - Weather,* and *Crawly Critters* activity guides.

THIS BUD'S FOR YOU

WHAT YOU NEED

- A fresh, white carnation
- Knife
- Drinking glass
- Water
- Red or blue food colouring
- Fresh celery stalk with leaves (optional)

WHAT TO DO

1. Cut about 2 cm off the bottom of a white carnation's stem.

2. Put the carnation in a glass half filled with water and a few drops of food colouring.

3. Leave the carnation in the glass for a few hours. Check it occasionally. What do you see? Does the colour gradually travel up to the petals?

4. When the colour has reached the petals, cut a small piece off the bottom of the carnation stem. What do you see?

WHAT'S GOING ON?

Liquids travel up plant and flower stems along little tubes. Can you see coloured spots along the edge of the flower stem where you cut it? These spots are the ends of fine tubes that water travels along to reach the petals. A stem allows water and nutrients to reach the leaves, where they are converted to plant food. The fine tubes in the roots, stems, and leaves of plants help to draw water from the ground to the top of even the tallest trees through "capillary action". Capillary action is the tendency of a liquid to be pulled into a very thin tube. The thinner the tube, the higher up the tube the liquid will be pulled. Capillary action is based on attraction between molecules, the same attraction that causes surface tension. When water is in a tiny tube, water molecules at the top are pulled up the tube and they then pull the molecules behind them.

WHAT ELSE YOU CAN DO

Cut the carnation stem lengthwise and try to follow a tube up to the petals. Try the activity again, but this time use the celery. What happens? Dip the end of a strip of paper towel into some water and watch the water creep slowly up the strip. The paper towel has long, narrow, tube-like gaps between its fibres, and the water travels up these gaps through capillary action.

THE SCIENCE HOTLINE
(A SERVICE OF THE CALGARY SCIENCE NETWORK)

WHO WE ARE
We are a link between schools, teachers, youth groups, community and scientists, engineers and technologists.

The Science Hotline
c/o Geological Survey of Canada
3303 - 33 Street N.W.
Calgary, Alberta   T2L 2A7

Tel: (403) 263-6226
Fax: (403) 230-8488
E-mail: scihot@cadvision.com
World Wide Web: www.cadvision.com/calg_sci_net

Meeting Place and Time
Meeting with Calgary Science Network every second Tuesday of the month.

WHAT WE DO
The Science Hotline keeps a database of hundreds of volunteers in the Calgary area. We can connect you with a scientist to augment your planned science activities. We can provide classroom speakers and demonstrators (science career awareness), science competition judges, information resources, field trip leaders, and workshops for teachers. There is no fee. Please call for further information and other available services, or E-mail us.

Additional Information
The Science Hotline is funded by the Science Alberta Foundation, which receives funding from Alberta Lotteries, Science Culture Canada grants, and other, private, donors.

Programs Offered
Preschool (limited), elementary, junior and senior high school, teacher training, community, youth groups.

Resources
Loans of some science materials to volunteers to help them with their hands-on presentations to students.

MYSTERIOUS MOULD

WHAT YOU NEED
- Ziplock bag
- slice of bread
- eyedropper or teaspoon

WHAT TO DO
1. Place the bread in the plastic bag.
2. Place 10 drops of water inside the bag and seal the zip lock.
3. Keep the bag in a dark, warm place for 3 to 5 days.
4. Observe the bread through the plastic. What changes can you see in the bread?

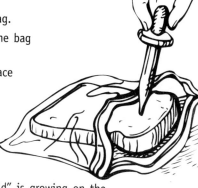

WHAT'S GOING ON?
A black, hairy structure called "mould" is growing on the bread. Mould is a form of fungus which can grow and reproduce very quickly. The mould produces very tiny cells with hard coverings called spores. These spores are smaller than dust particles and float through the air. Your slice of bread already had spores on it when placed in the plastic bag, and the water, warmth and darkness provided a good environment for the mould to grow.

Moulds have good and bad uses. Some make food taste and smell bad, but some foods depend on mould for their good taste (e.g., blue cheese). The greenish mould that forms on bread and oranges is used to make a medicine called penicillin, which has helped save many lives.

WHAT ELSE YOU CAN DO
Try using different kinds of bread (white, whole wheat, preservatives versus no preservatives, etc.) to find out which type allows the most mould to grow.

BE CAREFUL!
Some people are sensitive to mould and it can cause a serious allergic reaction. It is important that you keep the mouldy bread inside the sealed bag, just in case. Make sure you discard the bag and its contents after your observation.

SCOUTS CANADA - CALGARY REGIONAL COUNCIL

WHO WE ARE
We are a high profile and well respected national organization that helps children gain the confidence and skills they need to face life's challenges. From climbing rope to surfing the Internet, Scouting helps young people clear life's hurdles, be they physical, technological, social or intellectual. As a member of the World Scouting Movement, Scouts Canada also fosters global links. So if you thought Scouting was only about campfires and crafts—think again!

Scouts Canada
2140 Brownsea Drive N.W.
Calgary, Alberta

Tel: (403) 283-4993
Fax: (403) 283-6844
E-Mail: bob_s@telusplanet.net

Membership Fees
Average $50.00 per person per year.

WHAT WE DO
Our high profile comes from activities such as tree planting and community service events that demonstrate Scouting members' commitment to local, national and international communities. Scouting stimulates the mind and body by offering dynamic outdoor experiences, with activities ranging from gardening to model making. Members might master a challenging swim stroke, or learn to play a musical instrument, or visit zoos, libraries or planetariums. Learning to live in harmony with the natural environment is vital to all Scouting members. Activities such as hiking, backpacking, camping and exploring are linked to the respect and preservation of natural habitats. Scouting is a family affair and it creates a sense of shared accomplishment.

Resources
Books, newsletter, teacher kits, speakers, presentations, slide shows/videos/films, information sheets, portable exhibits, equipment.

Facilities
Auditorium, museum, exhibits, classroom, interpretive centre, library, bookstore and giftshop selling camping and outdoor supplies.

EARTHWORMS AND RAIN

WHAT YOU NEED

- 2 worm-ranch vivariums
- Aquarium gravel
- Sand
- Clay soil
- Topsoil
- Loose organic litter
- 20-40 live earthworms
- Water
- Timer

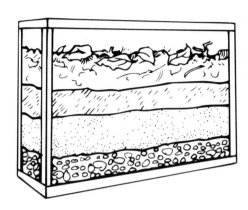

WHAT TO DO

1. Follow the diagram and set up the earthworm ranches on a tray.

2. Gently water your ranch until it begins to drain from the bottom of the frame onto the tray.

3. Place 20 earthworms on the surface, and wait a week.

4. Observe the earthworms' behaviour. When do they begin to move, to dig. What else are they doing?

5. Observe the worms for one week. What happens to the organic litter on the surface?

6. Pour water in the top of the vivarium and soak it until water drains out.

7. Note what changes occur and when. Be sure to note the time elapsed.

WHAT'S GOING ON?

Your vivarium acts like soil in the rain. You can observe the earthworms and their actions in the rain. You can also see how earthworms affect soil.

WHAT ELSE YOU CAN DO

When the water has stopped draining from the vivariums, put an incandescent light above them. What do the earthworms do?

SOCIETY OF EDUCATIONAL RESOURCE GROUPS (SERG)

WHO WE ARE

We are an umbrella organization for educational resource organizations in Calgary. Our members include any qualified organization that offers quality, curriculum-based educational programs.

The Society of Educational Resource Groups
P.O Box 1653, Station M
Calgary, Alberta   T2P 2L7

Tel: (403) 221-3739

WHAT WE DO

We help to promote and enhance understanding and appreciation of, as well as commitment to, natural and cultural resources. We provide educational programs for students and adults, assist teachers develop educational programs, assist with and provide professional development, and assist with and provide off-site curricular field studies or in-school presentations.

Resources

An annual directory of SERG members and programs that are available to schools or community groups is distributed to all Calgary and area schools.

MOVING ICE

WHAT YOU NEED
- A pan
- Ice cubes
- A toy

WHAT TO DO
1. Half-fill the pan with water. Add enough ice cubes so that the ice appears solid on the top.
2. Place the toy on the ice. Balance it so that it looks "safe".
3. Put your finger in the water at the edge of the pan and move it back and forth.
4. What happens to the toy?

WHAT'S GOING ON?
The ice may look safe and solid but you can see that the "solid" ice isn't really safe at all. Ice on a river or a lake can sometimes look solid even when it isn't. Waves in the water under the ice can make it move just like the ice in the pan.

WHAT ELSE YOU CAN DO
Think about skating on ice on a lake or river. What would you do if you saw a friend in the same situation as your toy?

SWIFT FOX CONSERVATION SOCIETY OF ALBERTA

WHO WE ARE
We are a non-profit society dedicated to fund-raising and education to support the extirpated Swift Fox returning to the Canadian prairies.

Swift Fox Conservation Society of Alberta
Box 46026, Inglewood P.O.
Calgary, Alberta   T2G 5H7

Tel: (403) 244-8144
Fax: (403) 244-8144
E-mail: idmcg@aol.com

Membership Fees
$10.00 per year.

WHAT WE DO
We provide funding for graduate field research on the swift fox, and for the swift fox census. We are currently working on establishing a web site. We occasionally have information booths in malls or at environmental fairs. We also assist students in gathering information, and send out information on request.

Resources
Videos, information sheets, portable exhibits, swift fox library.

CREATURES OF THE NIGHT

WHAT YOU NEED
- A natural area to take a walk in
- Regular or pen flashlights (red cellophane and masking tape)
- Fruit Roll-up
- 125 mL of sugar
- 250 mL of water
- Bug boxes
- Lamp without a shade and different colours of light bulbs
- An old white sheet

WHAT TO DO
1. Become familiar with the natural area by day and plan your route.
2. Before you take your night walk, prepare an insect snack so you can study moths and other insects while they are eating! Dissolve a Fruit Roll-up and 125 mL of sugar in 250 mL of water. Heat it until it turns into syrup. Paint the syrup on an easily identified tree at least 1 hour beforehand.
3. On a warm night, walk your planned route quietly. Keep all of your senses alert. Notice how long it takes your eyes to become adapted to the dark. (Red plastic covers on the flashlights will preserve your "night vision".)
4. Listen for the calls of nocturnal animals: owls hooting, crickets chirping, frogs croaking, coyotes howling, foxes yipping and yapping.
5. Use your flashlights to catch a glimpse of a swooping bat, a cat's eyes or evidence of other creatures. Examine low lying plants for spiders and nocturnal insects, some of which have compound eyes. These eyes reflect and refract light if you shine your penlight across them at 90 degrees.
6. Go to the "painted" tree you prepared earlier. How many different kinds of creatures can you see? Use your bug boxes to examine the creatures.

WHAT'S GOING ON?
Many people are frightened by creatures of the night because they can't see them. However, nocturnal animals are very much like animals of the day and wildlife watching at night can be a wonderful experience.

WHAT ELSE YOU CAN DO
Attach an old white sheet to the side of a building or tie it between some trees. Using a lamp without a shade, shine light on the sheet. How quickly do moths appear? Try red, yellow and blue lights. Which colours attract insects?

UNIVERSITY OF CALGARY, CAMPUS RECREATION - MINI-UNIVERSITY

WHO WE ARE

We are a unique fun-filled, educational program that provides children with practical "hands-on" experience in a variety of disciplines. Children are exposed to potential career avenues while obtaining a taste of University life. The program emphasizes creativity, personal development and enrichment.

Mini-University, The University of Calgary
PEA101 for Registration - Physical Education Building
2500 University Drive N.W.
Calgary, Alberta   T2N 1N4

Tel: (403) 220-7241
Fax: (403) 284-5867
E-mail: nrpitt@acs.ucalgary.ca

Membership Fees

$129.00 to $235.00, depending on length (one or two weeks).

Days/Hours

July through August, Monday to Friday, 9:00 a.m. to 4:00 p.m.

WHAT WE DO

We provide hands-on experience in many different subjects. The program is for children Grades 4 to 8 (ages 9 to 14) and provides them with the unique opportunity to become involved in personal growth and development in a comfortable, non-threatening environment. The goal of the program is to provide participants with the opportunity to grow and mature at the intellectual, social and emotional level and to develop lifetime leisure skills. The leaders and instructors are chosen for their ability to work with children in a creative and fun environment. The ratio of students to instructors is 8:1 in the classroom and 8:1 in the pool. Recreational activities are scheduled throughout the day.

Programs Offered

Elementary, junior high school.

MODEL FIRE EXTINGUISHER

Note: Adult supervision is required for this activity.

WHAT YOU NEED

- 375 mL plastic or glass bottle with a screw cap or cork
- Drinking straw (flex-straw)
- Plasticine
- Paper clip
- Thread
- Two-ply toilet paper
- Baking soda
- Vinegar
- Water

WHAT TO DO

1. Drill a hole through the bottle cap or cork just large enough to let the straw pass through it.

2. Push the straw through the cap so the long part is inside the bottle. Seal the straw to the cap with Plasticine making an airtight seal.

3. Pour about 100 mL of vinegar into the bottle and add water until the bottle is three-quarters full.

4. Separate the two thicknesses of a piece of toilet paper to create one very thin sheet of paper.

5. Using the sheet of paper made in Step 4, make a narrow bag tied at the top with about 10 cm of thread. Add about 5 mL of baking soda.

6. Lower the bag into the bottle taking care not to touch the liquid, and allow the excess thread to hang over the neck of the bottle.

7. Replace the cap so that the bag is left hanging in the bottle.

8. Put a paper clip on the upper end of the straw to reduce its diameter.

9. To activate the fire extinguisher, shake the bottle to wet the bag of baking soda, which will burst.

10. Quickly hold a lit match above the straw.

WHAT'S GOING ON?

The baking soda reacts with the vinegar to produce carbon dioxide gas which creates pressure. This forcibly ejects the water, vinegar, carbon dioxide mixture through the straw, extinguishing the flame. Air is made of several gases, including oxygen (O_2) and carbon dioxide (CO_2). While O_2 feeds flames, CO_2 kills them.

YOUNG SCIENTISTS OF CANADA

WHO WE ARE
We are an organization that encourages the involvement of young people in science through various scientific activities. The Young Scientists of Canada (YSC), is a part of the Youth Science Foundation.

Young Scientists of Canada, Calgary Chapter
P.O. Box 67150, Northland Village
Calgary, Alberta   T2L 2L2

Tel: (403) 247-2628
Fax: (403) 247-1739
E-mail: srchaudh@acs.ucalgary.ca

Meeting Place and Time
Call for information.

Membership Fees
Based on activities.

WHAT WE DO
Activities have included involvement in scientific demonstrations and science fairs, field trips and a range of other projects and programs developed by YSC members. The aim of the YSC is to stimulate scientific interest in young people by young people. Participation of adults through advisory roles is encouraged.

Programs Offered
Elementary, junior and senior high school.

Resources
Speakers, presentations.

WATER MIX UP

WHAT YOU NEED

- 5 or more glasses
- Spoon
- Hot water
- Cold water
- Salt
- 4 different colours of food colouring (e.g., blue, yellow, red, green)
- Corn syrup, cooking oil

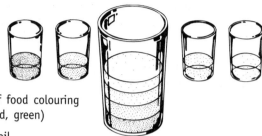

WHAT TO DO

1. Take four glasses. Put cold salt water in one, cold fresh water, hot salt water, and hot fresh water separately in the others.

2. Add drops of different colours to each glass and stir. Food colouring makes it easier to tell the liquids apart (it doesn't affect liquid density).

3. Take a clean glass and carefully pour in a layer of each liquid. Try cold salt water on the bottom; cold fresh water next; hot salt water next; and finally, hot fresh water. Be careful not to mix the layers as you pour. Add a new layer by tilting the glass slightly and running a new liquid along the inside.

4. Take another clean glass and try pouring the layers in a different order. What happens this time?

5. Experiment with different temperatures of water and different amounts of salt.

WHAT'S GOING ON?

The heavier a liquid, the greater its density. A liquid less dense than water will float on water; a liquid more dense will sink. If you compare hot and cold fresh water to hot and cold salt water, the order of density is: cold salt water (most dense)—cold fresh water—hot salt water—hot fresh water (least dense).

WHAT ELSE YOU CAN DO

Put different food colours (avoid yellow) in a glass of water and a glass of corn syrup. Make a liquid layer creation with oil on the top, water in the middle, and corn syrup on the bottom. Try adding the three liquids in different orders. Does changing the order change the final positions of the liquids in the glass? Did you discover that oil is less dense than water but corn syrup is more dense?

DAY TRIPS

The following facilities are either in Calgary or within a few hours' drive of Calgary, and offer various interesting interpretive programs and exhibits. Local telephone calls for Calgary are given without the (403) area code.

Aggie Days Tours, Calgary. Annual three-day educational agriculture program for students and teachers, held in the spring. Guided tours and hands-on learning centres. Contact Lorna MacMillan 261-9316 or fax 262-3067.

Alberta Birds of Prey Centre, Coaldale. Open to the public from May long weekend until Thanksgiving for guided tours and flying shows. Contact Wendy Slater (403) 345-4262.

Brooks Pheasant Hatchery, Brooks. Display and 15-minute film. Birds on display in summer. Contact Sharon Hampton 310-0000 then 362-4122.

Company of Adventurers, Calgary. Outdoor learning experiences for students and interpretive tours for the public. Prehistory, Eco-regions, Ecology and Wildplaces, Wildlife, Outdoor Pursuits and Special Interest Trips. Call for free brochure. Contact Bernie Woods 242-8725 or fax 246-9493.

County of Vulcan, Vulcan. For travelling education and fun while driving in Vulcan, pick up a free science activity kit to use on the Interactive Science Activity Sign Tour. Free copy of *Exploring a New Frontier* science activity guidebook also available. Contact Mary, Bev or Georgie, c/o Economic Development and Tourism (403) 485-2992 or fax (403) 485-2878.

Dinosaur Country Science Camps, Drumheller. Annual summer science camps for kids aged 9 to 13. Six days of science activities and participation in current research projects. Contact Camp Director, Tel./Fax.: (403) 823-2030.

Eagle Lake Campground, east of Calgary. Interpretive programs led by a former provincial park interpreter. Natural history, nature (bugs, birds, pond studies). Contact Leslie Pringle (403) 934-4283.

Frank Slide Interpretive Centre, Bellevue (west of Pincher Creek). Situated on the landslide site, the centre offers visitors a combination of walking trails over the slide and interpretive displays inside the centre. Tours of Frank and Bellevue mines also available. Tel.: 310-0000 then 562-7388.

Groundwork Natural Science Education, East Coulee (near Drumheller). The palaeontology, archaeology and natural history of Dinosaur Country are the focus of Family Day Camps and Badlands Science Adventures tours for schools and groups. Contact Robin Digby or Linda Ecklund Digby, Tel./Fax.: (403) 822-3976.

Head-Smashed-in-Buffalo Jump, Fort Macleod. The interpretive centre at this spectacular location is built into the cliff near an ancient Native buffalo run. Interpretive displays focus on local nature, prehistory and history. Contact Shirley Bruised Head 310-0000 then 553-2731, or 265-0048 in Calgary.

Helen Schuler Coulee Centre and Nature Reserve, Lethbridge. Self-guided trails in the nature reserve. Seasonal exhibit room. Sunday nature walks. Junior naturalists' program. Contact Sherry Feser (403) 320-3064.

Kananaskis Field Stations, Kananaskis Country, Mike Mappin (403) 673-3662, or 220-5355 in Calgary.

Kerry Wood Nature Centre, Red Deer. Interactive, professionally developed exhibits: walk-through glaciers, dioramas, simulated helicopter rides, all depicting the natural history of central Alberta. Children's discovery room with live animals. Centre is connected to 85 km of biking trails. Hiking trails. Naturalist interpretation programs. Open all year. Free. Contact Jim Robertson (403) 346-2010.

Natural History Museum, Banff. Small museum with nature, geology and mineralogy displays. Contact Alan or Joan Hall (403) 762-4747.

Reptile World, Drumheller. An amazing variety of reptile life is on display, from full-grown alligators to miniature toads. Knowledgeable staff give frequent demonstrations and answer questions. Contact Dave Bethel (403) 823-8623.

Royal Tyrrell Field Station, Dinosaur Provincial Park, Patricia (northeast of Brooks). Palaeontology museum and guided tours to the *Centrosaurus* bonebeds. Badlands Bus Tours into the natural preserve of the World Heritage Site. Tel.: 310-0000 then 378-4342.

Royal Tyrrell Museum of Palaeontology, Drumheller. World-class palaeontology museum with fascinating displays about Alberta's rich fossil resources and the history of life on Earth. Tel.: 310-0000 then 823-7707, or 294-1992 Calgary.

Spruce Meadows, Calgary. School tour program. Contact Jacinthe Carswell 974-4200 or fax 974-4266.

Western Heritage Centre, Cochrane. Public and school interpretive programs with environmental themes. Science programs (Grades 1 to 9). Veterinary technology; simulated calf surgery. Contact Lynn Munro 932-3514.

Yoho-Burgess Shale Foundation Guided Earth Science Hikes, Field, B.C. Strenuous, full-day, mountain hikes reward the traveller with spectacular views and a chance to see what Stephen Jay Gould called "the world's most important animal fossils". Reservations necessary. Tel.: 1-800-343-3006.

SCIENCE AND NATURE RESOURCES

CLUBS, SOCIETIES

PROFESSIONAL ORGANIZATIONS

PROFESSIONAL ORGANIZATIONS (CONT'D)

FACILITIES

OTHER RESOURCES

HANDS-ON ACTIVITIES

INDEX OF ACTIVITIES (CONT'D)

ALBERTA EDUCATION SCIENCE CURRICULUM LINKS

The following list contains page numbers for the activities in this guide that relate to teaching units in the Alberta Education elementary and junior high school science curriculum. For example, if you are teaching the Creating Colours unit in Grade 1, you can turn to pages 65, 67, 85 and 95 in this guide, to find extension activities to do with your students.

Grade 1
- Creating Colours, 65, 67, 85, 95
- Seasonal Changes, 99, 89, 107, 111, 137
- Building Things, 39
- Senses, 19, 51, 55, 99, 101, 123
- Needs of Animals and Plants, 23, 33, 79, 111, 113, 123

Grade 2
- Exploring Liquids, 63, 65, 85, 95, 119, 137, 143
- Buoyancy and Boats, 29, 137
- Magnetism, 73
- Hot and Cold Temperatures, 51, 109
- Small Crawling and Flying Creatures, 17, 25, 47, 49, 51, 71, 77, 79, 99, 123, 135, 139

Grade 3
- Rocks and Minerals, 9, 13, 31, 69, 83
- Building with a Variety of Materials, 23
- Testing Building Materials and Designs, 49, 115
- Hearing and Sound, 25, 35, 51, 103
- Animal Life Cycles, 99, 115

Grade 4
- Waste and Our World, 31, 65, 67, 91, 111
- Wheels and Levers, 21
- Building Devices and Vehicles that Move, 15, 21, 127
- Light and Shadows, 67, 85, 129, 139
- Plant Growth and Changes, 41, 61, 87, 89, 91, 113, 131, 133

Grade 5
- Electricity and Magnetism, 73
- Mechanisms Using Electricity, 97

DID WE MISS YOU?

If you would like to be included in the next *Calgary Science Fun Guide*, please fill in the form below, mail or fax it to Bare Bones Publishing, and we'll send you a questionnaire.

Name of Organization:

_____

Name of Contact Person:

_____

Mailing Address:

_____

_____

Postal Code:

_____

Telephone:

_____

Fax:

_____

Mail completed form to Bare Bones Publishing, Suite 355, 305-4625 Varsity Drive N.W., Calgary, Alberta T3A 0Z9, or fax to (403) 239-0563.

Science Fun Guides

Calgary Science Fun Guide (2nd edn.)
Compiled for the Calgary Science Network, the Calgary Science Fun Guide is the ideal reference for exploring science and nature in Calgary. Containing over 60 hands-on activities, it's the perfect book for budding scientists and their parents, teachers and group leaders.

ISBN 1-896865-02-X $14.95   160 p   softcover

Edmonton Science Fun Guide
An A to Z of where to go and what to do in Edmonton if your passion is science or nature. A superb source of over 60 neat hands-on activities that will open your eyes to the wonderful worlds of science, technology and nature.
ISBN 1-896865-00-3 $14.95   160 p   softcover

Greater Vancouver Science Fun Guide
The Greater Vancouver Science Fun Guide is full of places to go, clubs to join, and lots of things to see and do. It lists key organizations in the Lower Mainland involved in science and nature . . . from beekeeping to playing music in the symphony orchestra! This terrific resource guide puts you in touch with over 70 groups offering science experiences. Includes over 70 hands-on activities.

ISBN 0-9696095-9-0 $12.95   160 p   softcover

South Vancouver Island Earth Science Fun Guide
For all rock hounds and other earth science buffs! This comprehensive guide to South Vancouver Island's earth science resources is a must for visitors as well as locals. It contains essential information on over 50 clubs, organizations and facilities, as well as unique hands-on activities, written by local earth scientists.

ISBN 1-896865-01-1 $10.95   112 p   softcover

See order form on page 159